William (

Heroes of Science

William Garnett

Heroes of Science

1st Edition | ISBN: 978-3-75233-099-1

Place of Publication: Frankfurt am Main, Germany

Year of Publication: 2020

Outlook Verlag GmbH, Germany.

HEROES OF SCIENCE.

BY

WILLIAM GARNETT

PREFACE.

The following pages claim no originality, and no merits beyond that of bringing within reach of every boy and girl material which would otherwise be available only to those who had extensive libraries at their command, and much time at their disposal. In the schools and colleges in which the principles of physical science are well taught, the history of the discoveries whereby those principles have been established has been too much neglected. The series to which the present volume belongs is intended, in some measure, to meet this deficiency.

A complete history of physical science would, if it could be written, form a library of considerable dimensions. The following pages deal only with the biographies of a few distinguished men, who, by birth, were British subjects, and incidental allusions only are made to living philosophers; but, notwithstanding these narrow restrictions, the foundations of the Royal Society of London, of the American Philosophical Society, of the great Library of Pennsylvania, and of the Royal Institution, are events, some account of which comes within the compass of the volume. The gradual development of our knowledge of electricity, of the mechanical theory of heat, and of the undulatory theory of optics, will be found delineated in the biographies selected, though no continuous history is traced in the case of any one of these branches of physics.

The sources from which the matter contained in the following pages has been derived have been, in addition to the published works of the subjects of the several sketches, the following:—

"The Encyclopædia Britannica."

"Memoir of the Honourable Robert Boyle," by Thomas Birch, M.A., prefixed to the folio edition of his works, which was published in London in 1743.

"Life of Benjamin Franklin," from his own writings, by John Bigelow.

Dr. G. Wilson's "Life of Cavendish," which forms the first volume of the publications of the Cavendish Society; and the "Electrical Researches of the Hon. Henry Cavendish, F.R.S.," edited by the late Professor James Clerk Maxwell.

"The Life of Sir Benjamin Thompson, Count Rumford," by George E. Ellis, published by the American Academy of Arts and Sciences, in connection with the complete edition of his works.

"Memoir of Thomas Young," by the late Dean Peacock.

Dr. Bence Jones's "Life of Faraday;" and Professor Tyndall's "Faraday as a Discoverer."

"Life of James Clerk Maxwell," by Professor Lewis Campbell and William Garnett.

It is hoped that the perusal of the following sketches may prove as instructive to the reader as their preparation has been to the writer.

WM. GARNETT.

Newcastle-upon-Tyne,
December, 1885.

INTRODUCTION.

The dawn of true ideas respecting mechanics has been described in the volume of this series devoted to astronomers. At the time when the first of the following biographies opens there were a few men who held sound views respecting the laws of motion and the principles of hydrostatics. Considerable advance had been made in the subject of geometrical optics; the rectilinear propagation of light and the laws of reflection having been known to the Greeks and Arabians, whilst Willebrod Snellius, Professor of Mathematics at Leyden, had correctly enunciated the laws of refraction very early in the seventeenth century. Pliny mentions the action of a sphere of rock-crystal and of a glass globe filled with water in bringing light to a focus. Roger Bacon used segments of a glass sphere as lenses; and in the eleventh century Alhazen made many measurements of the angles of incidence and refraction, though he did not succeed in discovering the law. Huyghens developed to a great extent the undulatory theory; while Newton at the same time made great contributions to the subject of geometrical optics, decomposed white light by means of a prism, investigated the colours of thin plates, and some cases of diffraction, and speculated on the nature, properties, and functions of the ether, which was equally necessary to the corpuscular as to the undulatory theory of light, if any of the phenomena of interference were to be explained. The velocity of light was first measured by Roemer, in 1676. The camera obscura was invented by Baptista Porta, a wealthy Neapolitan, in 1560; and Kepler explained the action of the eye as an optical instrument, in 1604. Antonio de Dominis, Archbishop of Spalatro, discovered the fringe of colours produced by sunlight once reflected from the interior of a globe of water, and this led, in Newton's hands, to the complete explanation of the rainbow.

The germ of the mechanical theory of heat is to be found in the writings of Lord Bacon. The first thermometers which were blown in glass with a bulb and tube hermetically sealed, were made by a craftsman in Florence, in the time of Torricelli. The graduations on these thermometers were made by attaching little beads of coloured glass to their stems, and they were carried about Europe by members of the Florentine Academy, in order to learn whether ice melted at the same temperature in all latitudes.

In electricity the attraction of light bodies by amber when rubbed, was known at least six hundred years before the Christian era, and the shocks of the torpedo were described by Pliny and by Aristotle; but the phenomena were not associated in men's minds until recent times. Dr. Gilbert, of Colchester, Physician to Queen Elizabeth, may be regarded as the founder of the modern

4

science. He distinguished two classes of bodies, viz. electrics, or those which would attract light bodies when rubbed; and non-electrics, or those which could not be so excited. The first electric machine was constructed by Otto von Guericke, the inventor of the Magdeburg hemispheres, who mounted a ball of sulphur so that it could be made rapidly to rotate while it was excited by the friction of the hand. He observed the repulsion which generally follows the attraction of a light body by an electrified object after the two have come in contact. He also noticed that certain bodies placed near to electrified bodies possessed similar powers of attraction to those of the electrified bodies themselves. Newton replaced the sulphur globe of Otto von Guericke by a globe of glass. Stephen Gray discovered the conduction of electricity, in 1729, when he succeeded in transmitting a charge to a distance of 886 feet along a pack-thread suspended by silk strings so as to insulate it from the earth. Desaguliers showed that Gilbert's "electrics" were simply those bodies which could not conduct electricity, while all conductors were "non-electrics;" and Dufay showed that all bodies could be electrified by friction if supported on insulating stands. He also showed that there were two kinds of electrification, and called one *vitreous*, the other *resinous*. Gray, Hawksbee, and Dr. Wall all noticed the similarity between lightning and the electric discharge. The prime conductor was first added to the electric machine by Boze, of Wittenberg; and Winkler, of Leipsic, employed a cushion instead of the hand to produce friction against the glass. The accumulation of electricity in the Leyden jar was discovered accidentally by Cuneus, a pupil of Muschenbroeck, of Leyden, about 1745, while attempting to electrify water in a bottle held in his hand. A nail passed through the cork, by which the electricity was communicated to the water. On touching the nail after charging the water, he received the shock of the Leyden jar. This brings the history of electrical discovery down to the time of Franklin.

ROBERT BOYLE.

Robert Boyle was descended from a family who, in Saxon times, held land in the county of Hereford, and whose name in the Doomsday Book is written Biuvile. His father was Richard Boyle, Earl of Cork, to whom the fortunes of the family were largely due. Richard Boyle was born in the city of Canterbury, October 3, 1566. He was educated at Bene't College (now Corpus Christi College), Cambridge, and afterwards became a member of the Middle Temple. Finding his means insufficient for the prosecution of his legal studies, he determined to seek his fortune abroad. In 1595 he married, at Limerick, one of the daughters of William Apsley, who brought him land of the value of £500 per annum. In his autobiography the Earl of Cork writes:—

> When first I arrived at Dublin, in Ireland, the 23rd of June 1588, all my wealth then was twenty-seven pounds three shillings in money, and two tokens which my mother had given me, viz. a diamond ring, which I have ever since and still do wear, and a bracelet of gold worth about ten pounds; a taffety doublet cut with and upon taffety, a pair of black velvet breeches laced, a new Milan fustian suit laced and cut upon taffety, two cloaks, competent linen, and necessaries, with my rapier and dagger. And since, the blessing of God, whose heavenly providence guided me hither, hath enriched my weak estate, in beginning with such a fortune, as I need not envy any of my neighbours, and added no care or burthen of my conscience thereunto. And the 23rd of June, 1632, I have served my God, Queen Elizabeth, King James, and King Charles, full forty-four years, and so long after as it shall please God to enable me.

Richard Boyle's property in Ireland increased so rapidly that he was accused to Queen Elizabeth of receiving pay from some foreign power. When about to visit England in order to clear himself of this charge, the rebellion in Munster broke out; his lands were wasted, and his income for the time destroyed. Reaching London, he returned to his old chambers in the Middle Temple, until he entered the service of the Earl of Essex, to whom the government of Ireland had been entrusted. The charges against him were then resumed, and he was made a prisoner, and kept in confinement until the Earl of Essex had gone over to Ireland. At length he obtained a hearing before the queen, who fully acquitted him of the charges, gave him her hand to kiss, and promised to employ him in her own service; at the same time she dismissed Sir Henry Wallop, who was Treasurer for Ireland, and prominent among Boyle's accusers, from his office.

A few days afterwards, Richard Boyle was appointed by the queen Clerk to the Council of Munster, and having purchased a ship of Sir Walter Raleigh, he returned to Ireland with ammunition and provisions.

"Then, as Clerk of the Council, I attended the Lord President in all his employments, and waited upon him at the siege of Kingsale, and was employed by his Lordship to her Majesty, with the news of that happy victory; in which employment I made a speedy expedition to the court; for I left my Lord President at Shannon Castle, near Corke, on the Monday morning, about two of the clock, and the next day, being Tuesday, I delivered my packet, and supped with Sir Robert Cecil, being then principal Secretary of State, at his house in the Strand; who, after supper, held me in discourse till two of the clock in the morning; and by seven that morning called upon me to attend him to the court, where he presented me to her Majesty in her bed-chamber, who remembered me, calling me by my name, and giving me her hand to kiss, telling me that she was glad that I was the happy man to bring the first news of that glorious victory ... and so I was dismissed with grace and favour."

In reading of this journey from Cork to London, it is almost necessary to be reminded that it took place two hundred and fifty years before the introduction of steam-boats and railways. At the close of the rebellion, Richard Boyle purchased from Sir Walter Raleigh all his lands in Munster; and on July 25, 1603, he married his second wife, Catharine, the only daughter of Sir Geoffrey Fenton, principal Secretary of State, and Privy Councillor in Ireland, "with whom I never demanded any marriage portion, neither promise of any, it not being in my consideration; yet her father, after my marriage, gave me one thousand pounds in gold with her. But that gift of his daughter unto me I must ever thankfully acknowledge as the crown of all my blessings; for she was a most religious, virtuous, loving, and obedient wife unto me all the days of her life." He was knighted by the Lord Deputy of Ireland, Sir George Carew, on his wedding-day; was sworn Privy Councillor of State of the Kingdom of Ireland in 1612; created Lord Boyle, Baron of Youghall, September 29, 1616; Lord Viscount of Dungarvon and Earl of Cork, October 26, 1620; one of the Lords Justices of Ireland, with a salary of £1200 per annum, in 1629; and Lord High Treasurer of Ireland, November 9, 1631.

Robert Boyle, the seventh son of the Earl of Cork, was born January 25, 1627. His mother died February 16, 1630. The earl lived in prosperity in Ireland till the breaking out of the rebellion in 1641, and died at Youghall in September, 1643. It is said that when Cromwell saw the vast improvements which the earl had made on his estate in Munster, he declared that "if there had been an Earl of Cork in every province, it would have been impossible for the Irish to have raised a rebellion."

At a very early age Robert was sent by his father to a country nurse, "who, by early inuring him, by slow degrees, to a coarse but cleanly diet, and to the usual passion of the air, gave him so vigorous a complexion that both hardships were made easy to him by custom, and the delights of conveniences and ease were endeared to him by their rarity." Making the acquaintance of some children who stuttered in their speech, he, by imitation, acquired the same habit, "so contagious and catching are men's faults, and so dangerous is the familiar commerce of those condemnable customs, that, being imitated but in jest, come to be learned and acquired in earnest." Before going to school he studied French and Latin, and showed considerable aptitude for scholarship. He was then sent to Eton, where his master took much notice of him, and "would sometimes give him unasked play-days, and oft bestow upon him such balls and tops and other implements of idleness as he had taken away from others that had unduly used them."

While at school, in the early morning, a part of the wall of the bedroom, with the bed, chairs, books, and furniture of the room above, fell on him and his brother. "His brother had his band torn about his neck, and his coat upon his back, and his chair crushed and broken under him; but by a lusty youth, then accidentally in the room, was snatched from out the ruins, by which [Robert] had, in all probability, been immediately oppressed, had not his bed been curtained by a watchful Providence, which kept all heavy things from falling on it; but the dust of the crumbled rubbish raised was so thick that he might there have been stifled had not he remembered to wrap his head in the sheet, which served him as a strainer, through which none but the purer air could find a passage." At Eton he spent nearly four years, "in the last of which he forgot much of that Latin he had got, for he was so addicted to more solid parts of knowledge that he hated the study of bare words naturally, as something that relished too much of pedantry to consort with his disposition and designs." On leaving Eton he joined his father at Stalbridge, in Dorsetshire, and was sent to reside with "Mr. W. Douch, then parson of that place," who took the supervision of his studies. Here he renewed his acquaintance with Latin, and devoted some attention to English verse, spending some of his idle hours in composing verses, "most of which, the day he came of age, he sacrificed to Vulcan, with a design to make the rest perish by the same fate." A little later he returned to his father's house in Stalbridge, and was placed under the tutelage of a French gentleman, who had been tutor to two of his brothers.

In October, 1638, Robert Boyle and his brother were sent into France. After a short stay at Lyons, they reached Geneva, where Robert remained with his tutor for about a year and three quarters. During his residence here an incident occurred which he regarded as the most important event of his life, and which we therefore give in his own words.

"To frame a right apprehension of this, you must understand that, though his inclinations were ever virtuous, and his life free from scandal and inoffensive, yet had the piety he was master of already so diverted him from aspiring unto more, that Christ, who long had lain asleep in his conscience (as He once did in the ship), must now, as then, be waked by a storm. For at a time which (being the very heat of summer) promised nothing less, about the dead of night, that adds most terror to such accidents, [he] was suddenly waked in a fright with such loud claps of thunder (which are oftentimes very terrible in those hot climes and seasons), that he thought the earth would owe an ague to the air, and every clap was both preceded and attended with flashes of lightning, so frequent and so dazzling that [he] began to imagine them the sallies of that fire that must consume the world. The long continuance of that dismal tempest, where the winds were so loud as almost drowned the noise of the very thunder, and the showers so hideous as almost quenched the lightning ere it could reach his eyes, confirmed him in his apprehensions of the day of judgment's being at hand. Whereupon the consideration of his unpreparedness to welcome it, and the hideousness of being surprised by it in an unfit condition, made him resolve and vow that, if his fears were that night disappointed, all his further additions to his life should be more religiously and watchfully employed. The morning came, and a serene, cloudless sky returned, when he ratified his determinations so solemnly, that from that day he dated his conversion, renewing, now he was past danger, the vow he had made whilst he believed himself to be in it; and though his fear was (and he blushed it was so) the occasion of his resolution of amendment, yet at least he might not owe his more deliberate consecration of himself to piety to any less noble motive than that of its own excellence."

After leaving Geneva, he crossed the Alps and travelled through Northern Italy. Here he spent much time in learning Italian; "the rest of his spare hours he spent in reading the modern history in Italian, and the new paradoxes of the great stargazer Galileo, whose ingenious books, perhaps because they could not be so otherwise, were confuted by a decree from Rome; his highness the Pope, it seems, presuming, and that justly, that the infallibility of his chair extended equally to determine points in philosophy as in religion, and loth to have the stability of that earth questioned in which he had established his kingdom."

Having visited Rome, he at length returned to France, and was detained at

Marseilles, awaiting a remittance from the earl to enable him to continue his travels. Through some miscarriage, the money which the earl sent did not arrive, and Robert and his brother had to depend on the credit of the tutor to procure the means to enable them to return home. They reached England in the summer of 1644, "where we found things in such confusion that, although the manor of Stalbridge were, by my father's decease, descended unto me, yet it was near four months before I could get thither." On reaching London, Robert Boyle resided for some time with his sister, Lady Ranelagh, and was thus prevented from entering the Royalist Army. Later on he returned for a short time to France; visited Cambridge in December, 1645, and then took up his residence at Stalbridge till May, 1650, where he commenced the study of chemistry and natural philosophy.

It was in October, 1646, that Boyle first made mention of the "*invisible college*," which afterwards developed into the Royal Society. Writing to a Fellow of Magdalen College, Cambridge, in February, 1647, he says, "The corner-stones of the *invisible*, or, as they term themselves, the *philosophical college*, do now and then honour me with their company." It appears that a desire to escape from the troubles of the times had induced several persons to take refuge in philosophical pursuits, and, meeting together to discuss the subjects of their study, they formed the "invisible college." Boyle says, "I will conclude their praises with the recital of their chiefest fault, which is very incident to almost all good things, and that is, that there is not enough of them." Dr. Wallis, one of the first members of the society, states that Mr. Theodore Hooke, a German of the Palatinate, then resident in London, "gave the first occasion and first suggested those meetings and many others. These meetings we held sometimes at Dr. Goddard's lodging, in Wood Street (or some convenient place near), on occasion of his keeping an operator in his house, for grinding glasses for telescopes and microscopes, and sometimes at a convenient place in Cheapside; sometimes at Gresham College, or some place near adjoining. Our business was (precluding theology and State affairs) to discourse and consider of philosophical inquiries, and such as related thereunto; as physic, anatomy, geometry, astronomy, navigation, statics, magnetics, chemics, mechanics, and natural experiments, with the state of these studies as then cultivated at home and abroad. About the year 1648-49 some of us being removed to Oxford, first Dr. Wilkins, then I, and soon after Dr. Goddard, our company divided. Those in London continued to meet there as before, and we with them when we had occasion to be there. And those of us at Oxford, with Dr. Ward, since Bishop of Salisbury, Dr. Ralph Bathurst, now President of Trinity College in Oxford, Dr. Petty, since Sir William Petty, Dr. Willis, then an eminent physician in Oxford, and divers others, continued such meetings in Oxford, and brought those studies into fashion there;

meeting first at Dr. Petty's lodgings, in an apothecary's house, because of the convenience of inspecting drugs and the like, as there was occasion; and after his remove to Ireland (though not so constantly) at the lodgings of Dr. Wilkins, then Warden of Wadham College; and after his removal to Trinity College in Cambridge, at the lodgings of the Honourable Mr. Robert Boyle, then resident for divers years in Oxford. These meetings in London continued, and after the king's return, in 1660, were increased with the accession of divers worthy and honourable persons, and were afterwards incorporated by the name of the *Royal Society*, and so continue to this day."

Boyle was only about twenty years of age when he wrote his "Free Discourse against Swearing;" his "Seraphic Love; or, Some Motives and Incentives to the Love of God;" and his "Essay on Mistaken Modesty." "Seraphic Love" was the last of a series of treatises on love, but the only one of the series that he published, as he considered the others too trifling to be published alone or in conjunction with it. In a letter to Lady Ranelagh, he refers to his laboratory as "a kind of Elysium," and there were few things which gave him so much pleasure as his furnaces and philosophical experiments. In 1652 he visited Ireland, returning in the following summer. In the autumn he was again obliged to visit Ireland, and remained there till the summer of 1654, though residence in that country was far from agreeable to him. He styled it "a barbarous country, where chemical spirits were so misunderstood, and chemical instruments so unprocurable, that it was hard to have any hermetic thoughts in it." On his return he settled in Oxford, and there his lodgings soon became the centre of the scientific life of the university. Boyle and his friends may be regarded as the pioneers of experimental philosophy in this country. To Boyle the methods of Aristotle appeared little more than discussions on words; for a long time he refused to study the philosophy of Descartes, lest he should be turned aside from reasoning based strictly on the results of experiment. The method pursued by these philosophers had been fully discussed by Lord Bacon, but at best his experimental methods, though most complete and systematic, existed only upon paper, and it was reserved for Boyle and his friends to put the Baconian philosophy into actual practice.

It was during his residence at Oxford that he invented the air-pump, which was afterwards improved for him by Hooke, and with which he conducted most of those experiments on the "spring" and weight of the air, which led up to the investigations that have rendered his name inseparably connected with "the gaseous laws." The experiments of Galileo and of Torricelli had shown that the pressure of the air was capable of supporting a column of water about thirty-four feet in height, or a column of mercury nearly thirty inches high. The younger Pascal, at the request of Torricelli, had carried a barometer to the summit of the Puy de Dome, and demonstrated that the height of the column of mercury supported by the air diminishes as the altitude is increased. Otto von Guericke had constructed the Magdeburg hemispheres, and shown that, when exhausted, they could not be separated by sixteen horses, eight pulling one way and eight the other. He was aware that the same traction could have been produced by eight horses if one of the hemispheres had been attached to a fixed obstacle; but, with the instincts of a popular lecturer, he considered that the spectacle would thus be rendered less striking, and it was prepared for the king's entertainment. Boyle wished for an air-pump with an aperture in the receiver sufficiently large for the introduction of various objects, and an arrangement for exhausting it without filling the receiver with water or otherwise interfering with the objects placed therein. His apparatus consisted of a large glass globe capable of containing about three gallons or thereabouts, terminating in an open tube below, and with an aperture of about four inches diameter at the top. Around this aperture was cemented a turned brass ring, the inner surface being conical, and into this conical seat was fitted a brass plate with a thick rim, but drilled with a small hole in the centre. To this hole, which was also conical, was fitted a brass stopper, which could be turned round when the receiver was exhausted. By attaching a string to this stopper, which was so long as to enter the receiver to the depth of two or three inches, and turning the stopper in its seat, the string could be wound up, and thus objects could be moved within the receiver. The tube at the bottom of the receiver communicated with a stop-cock, and this with the upper end of the pumpbarrel, which was inverted, so that this stop-cock, which was at the top of the barrel, took the place of the foot-valve. The piston was solid, made of wood, and surrounded with sole leather, which was kept well greased. There being no valve in the piston, it was necessary to place an exhaust-valve in the upper end of the cylinder. This consisted of a small brass plug closing a conical hole so that it could be removed at pleasure. The construction of the cylinder was, therefore, similar to that of an ordinary force-pump, except that the valves had to be moved by hand (as in the early forms of the steam-engine). The piston was raised and depressed by means of a rack and pinion. The pumps could be used either for exhausting the receiver or for forcing air into it, according to the order in which the "valves" were opened. If the stop-cock communicating with the receiver were open while the piston was being drawn down, and the brass plug removed so as to open the exhaust-valve when the piston was being forced up, the receiver would gradually be exhausted. If the brass plug were removed during the descent of the piston, and the stop-cock opened during its ascent, air would be forced into the receiver. In the latter case it was necessary to take special precautions to prevent the brass plate at the top of the receiver being raised from its seat. All joints were made air-tight with "diachylon," and when, through the bursting of a glass bulb within it, the receiver became cracked, the crack was rendered air-tight by the same means. Other receivers of smaller capacity were also provided, on account of the greater readiness with which they could be exhausted.

With this apparatus Boyle carried out a long series of experiments. He could reduce the pressure in the large receiver to somewhat less than that corresponding to an inch of mercury, or about a foot of water. Squeezing a bladder so as to expel nearly all the air, tying the neck, and then introducing it into the receiver, he found, on working the pump, that the bladder swelled so that at length it became completely distended. In order to account for this great expansibility, Boyle pictured the constitution of the air in the following way. He supposed the air to consist of separate particles, each resembling a spiral spring, which became tightly wound when exposed to great pressure, but which expanded so as to occupy a larger circle when the pressure was diminished. Each of these little spirals he supposed to rotate about a diameter so as to exclude every other body from the sphere in which it moved. Increasing the length of the diameter tenfold would increase the volume of one of these spheres, and therefore the volume of the gas, a thousandfold. Possibly this was only intended as a mental illustration, exhibiting a mechanism by which very great expansion might conceivably be produced, and scarcely pretending to be considered a *theory* of the constitution of the air. Boyle's first idea seems to have been derived from a lock of wool in which the elasticity of each fibre caused the lock to expand after it had been compressed in the hand. In another passage he speaks of the air as consisting of a number of bodies capable of striking against a surface exposed to them. He demonstrated the weight of the air by placing a delicate balance within the receiver, suspending from one arm a bladder half filled with water, and balancing it with brass weights. On exhausting the air, the bladder preponderated, and, by repeating the experiment with additional weights on the other arm until a balance was effected in the exhausted receiver, he determined the amount of the preponderance. In another experiment he compressed air in a bladder by tying a pack-thread round it, balanced it from one arm of his balance in the open air; then, pricking the bladder so as to relieve the pressure, he found that with the escape of the compressed air the weight diminished.

One of the most important of his experiments with the air-pump was the following. He placed within the receiver the cistern of a mercurial barometer, the tube of which was made to pass through the central hole in the brass plate, from which the stopper had been removed. The space around the tube was filled up with cement, and the receiver exhausted. At each stroke of the pump the mercury in the barometer tube descended, but through successively diminishing distances, until at length it stood only an inch above the mercury in the cistern. The experiment was then repeated with a tube four feet long and filled with water. This constituted the nineteenth experiment referred to later on. A great many strokes of the pump had to be made before the water began to descend. At length it fell till the surface in the tube stood only about a foot above that in the tank. Placing vessels of ordinary spring-water and of distilled rain-water in the receiver, he found that, after the exhaustion had reached a certain stage, bubbles of gas were copiously evolved from the spring-water, but not from the distilled water. On another occasion he caused warm water to boil by a few strokes of the pump; and, continuing the exhaustion, the water was made to boil at intervals until it became only lukewarm. The experiment was repeated with several volatile liquids. He also noticed the cloud formed in the receiver when the air was allowed rapidly to expand; but the mechanical theory of heat had not then made sufficient progress to enable him to account for the condensation by the loss of heat due to the work done by the expanding air. The very minute accuracy of his observations is conspicuous in the descriptions of most of his experiments. That the air is the usual medium for the conveyance of sound was shown by suspending a watch by a linen thread within the receiver. On exhausting the air, the ticking of the watch ceased to be heard. A pretty experiment consisted in placing a bottle of a certain fuming liquid within the receiver; on exhausting the air, the fumes fell over the neck of the bottle and poured over the stand on which it was placed like a stream of water. Another experiment, the thirty-second, is worthy of mention on account of the use to which it was afterwards applied in the controversy respecting the cause of suction. The receiver, having been exhausted, was removed from the cylinder, the stop-cock being turned off, and a small brass valve, to which a scale-pan was attached, was placed just under the aperture of the tube below the stop-cock. On turning the latter, the stream of air raised the valve, closing the aperture, and the atmospheric pressure supported it until a considerable weight had been placed in the scale-pan. Because the receiver could not be exhausted so thoroughly as the pump-cylinder, Boyle attempted to measure the pressure of the air by determining what weight could be supported by the piston. He found first that a weight of twenty-eight pounds suspended directly from the piston was sufficient to overcome friction when air was admitted above the piston. When the access of air to the top of the piston was prevented, more than one hundred pounds additional weight was required to draw down the piston. The diameter of the cylinder was about three inches.

Boyle's style of reasoning is well illustrated by the following from his paper on "The Spring of the Air:"—

"In the next place, these experiments may teach us what to judge of the vulgar axiom received for so many ages as an undoubted truth in the peripatetick schools, that Nature abhors and flieth a vacuum, and that to such a degree that no human power (to go no higher) is able to make one in the universe; wherein heaven and earth would change places, and all its other bodies rather act contrary to their own nature than suffer it…. It will not easily, then, be intelligibly made out how hatred or aversation, which is a passion of the soul, can either for a vacuum or any other object be supposed to be in water, or such like inanimate body, which cannot be presumed to know when a vacuum would ensue, if they did not bestir themselves to prevent it; nor to be so generous as to act contrary to what is most conducive to their own particular preservation for the public good of the universe. As much, then, of intelligible and probable truth as is contained in this metaphorical expression seems to amount but to this—that by the wise Author of nature (who is justly said to have made all things in number, weight, and measure) the universe, and the parts of it, are so contrived that it is hard to make a vacuum in it, as if they studiously conspired to prevent it. And how far this itself may be granted deserves to be further considered.

"For, in the next place, our experiments seem to teach that the supposed aversation of Nature to a vacuum is but accidental, or in consequence, partly of the weight and fluidity, or, at least, fluxility of the bodies here below; and partly, and perhaps principally, of the air, whose restless endeavour to expand itself every way makes it either rush in itself or compel the interposed bodies into all spaces where it finds no greater resistance than it can surmount. And that in those motions which are made *ob fugam vacui* (as the common phrase is), bodies act without such generosity and consideration as is wont to be ascribed to them, is apparent enough in our thirty-second experiment, where the torrent of air, that seemed to strive to get into the emptied receiver, did plainly prevent its own design, by so impelling the valve as to make it shut the only orifice the air was to get [in] at. And if afterwards either Nature or the internal air had a design the external air should be attracted, they seemed to prosecute it very unwisely by continuing to suck the valve so strongly, when they found that by that suction the valve itself could not be drawn in; whereas, by forbearing to suck, the valve would, by its own weight, have fallen down and suffered the excluded air to return freely, and to fill again the exhausted vessel….

"And as for the care of the public good of the universe ascribed to dead and stupid bodies, we shall only demand why, in our nineteenth experiment, upon the exsuction of the ambient air, the water deserted the upper half of the glass tube, and did not ascend to fill it up till the external air was let in upon it. Whereas, by its easy and sudden rejoining that upper part of the tube, it appeared both that there was then much space devoid of air, and that the water might, with small or no resistance, have ascended into it, if it could have done so without the impulsion of the readmitted air; which, it seems, was necessary to mind the water of its formerly neglected duty to the universe."

Boyle then goes on to explain the phenomena correctly by the pressure of the air. Elsewhere he accounts for the diminished pressure on the top of a mountain by the diminished weight of the superincumbent column of air.

The treatise on "The Spring of the Air" met with much opposition, and Boyle considered it necessary to defend his doctrine against the objections of Franciscus Linus and Hobbes. In this defence he described the experiment in connection with which he is most generally remembered. Linus had admitted that the air might possess a certain small amount of elasticity, but maintained that the force with which mercury rose in a barometer tube was due mainly to a totally different action, as though a string were pulling upon it from above. This was his funicular hypothesis. Boyle undertook to show that the pressure of the air might be made to support a much higher column of mercury than that of the barometer. To this end he took a glass tube several feet in length, and bent so as to form two vertical legs connected below. The shorter leg was little more than a foot long, and hermetically closed at the top. The longer leg was nearly eight feet in length, and open at the top. The tube was suspended by strings upon the staircase, the bend at the bottom pressing lightly against the bottom of a box placed to receive the mercury employed in case of accident. Each leg of the tube was provided with a paper scale. Mercury was poured in at the open end, the tube being tilted so as to allow some of the air to escape from the shorter limb until the mercury stood at the same level in both legs when the tube was vertical. The length of the closed tube occupied by the air was then just twelve inches. The height of the barometer was about 29-1/8 inches. Mercury was gently poured into the open limb by one operator, while another watched its height in the closed limb. The results of the experiments are given in the table on the opposite page.

In this table the third column gives the result of adding to the second column the height of the barometer, which expresses in inches of mercury the pressure of the air on the free surface of the mercury in the longer limb. The fourth column gives the total pressure, in inches of mercury, on the hypothesis that the pressure of the air varies inversely as the volume. The agreement between the third and fourth columns is very close, considering the roughness of the experiment and that no trouble appears to have been taken to *calibrate* the shorter limb of the tube, and justified Boyle in concluding that the hypothesis referred to expresses the relation between the volume and pressure of a given mass of air.

Length of closed tube occupied by air.	Height of mercury in open tube above that in closed tube.	Total pressure on air in inches of mercury.	Total pressure according to Boyle's law.
12	0	29-2/16	29-2/16
11-1/2	1-7/16	30-9/16	30-6/16
11	2-13/16	31-15/16	31-12/16
10-1/2	4-6/16	33-8/16	33-1/7
10	6-3/16	35-5/16	35
9-1/2	7-14/16	37	36-15/19
9	10-1/16	39-3/16	38-7/8
8-1/2	12-8/16	41-10/16	41-2/17
8	15-1/16	44-3/16	43-11/16
7-1/2	17-15/16	47-1/16	46-3/5
7	21-3/16	50-5/16	50
6-1/2	25-3/16	54-5/16	53-10/13
6	29-11/16	58-13/16	58-2/8
5-3/4	32-3/16	61-5/16	60-13/23
5-1/2	34-15/16	64-1/16	63-6/11
5-1/4	37-15/16	67-1/16	66-4/7
5	41-9/16	70-11/16	70
4-3/4	45	74-2/16	73-11/19
4-1/2	48-12/16	77-14/16	77-2/3
4-1/4	53-11/16	82-13/16	82-4/17
4	58-2/16	87-14/16	87-1/8
3-3/4	63-15/16	93-1/16	93-1/5
3-1/2	71-5/16	100-7/16	99-6/7
3-1/4	78-11/16	107-13/16	107-7/13
3	88-7/16	117-9/16	116-4/8

To extend the investigation so as to include expansion below atmospheric pressure, a different apparatus was employed. It consisted of a glass tube about six feet in length, closed at the lower end and filled with mercury. Into this bath of mercury was plunged a length of quill tube, and the upper end was sealed with wax. When the wax and air in the tube had cooled, a hot pin was passed through the wax, making a small orifice by which the amount of air in the tube was adjusted so as to occupy exactly one inch of its length as measured by a paper scale attached thereto, after again sealing the wax. The quill tube was then raised, and the height of the surface of the mercury in the tube above that in the bath noticed, together with the length of the tube occupied by the air. The difference between the height of the barometer and the height of the mercury in the tube above that in the bath gave the pressure on the imprisoned air in inches of mercury. The result showed that the volume varied very nearly in the inverse ratio of the pressure. A certain amount of air, however, clung to the sides of the quill tube when immersed in the mercury, and no care was taken to remove it by boiling the mercury or otherwise; in consequence of this, as the mercury descended, this air escaped and joined the rest of the air in the tube. This made the pressure rather greater than it should have been towards the end of the experiment, and when the tube was again pressed down into the bath it was found that, when the surfaces of the mercury within and without the tube were at the same level, the air occupied nearly 1-1/8 inch instead of one inch of the tube. These experiments first established the truth of the great law known as "Boyle's law," which states that *the volume of a given mass of a perfect gas varies inversely as the pressure to which it is exposed.*

Another experiment, to show that the pressure of the air was the cause of suction, Boyle succeeded in carrying out at a later date. Two discs of marble were carefully polished, so that when a little spirit of turpentine was placed between them the lower disc, with a pound weight suspended from it, was supported by the upper one. The apparatus was introduced into the air-pump, and a considerable amount of shaking proved insufficient to separate the discs. After sixteen strokes of the pump, on opening the communication between the receiver and cylinder, when no mechanical vibration occurred, the discs separated.

Upon the Restoration in 1660, the Earl of Clarendon, who was Lord Chancellor of England, endeavoured to persuade Boyle to enter holy orders, urging the interest of the Church as the chief motive for the proceeding. This made some impression upon Boyle, but he declined for two reasons—first, because he thought that he would have a greater influence for good if he had no share in the patrimony of the Church; and next, because he had never felt "an inward motion to it by the Holy Ghost."

In 1649 an association was incorporated by Parliament, to be called "the President and Society for the Propagation of the Gospel in New England," whose object should be "to receive and dispose of moneys in such manner as shall best and principally conduce to the preaching and propagating the gospel among the natives, and for the maintenance of schools and nurseries of learning for the education of the children of the natives; for which purpose a general collection was appointed to be made in and through all the counties, cities, towns, and parishes of England and Wales, for a charitable contribution, to be as the foundation of so pious and great an undertaking." The society was revived by special charter in 1661, and Boyle was appointed president, an office he continued to hold until shortly before his death. The society afterwards enlarged its sphere of operations, and became the Society for the Propagation of the Gospel in Foreign Parts.

In the same year (1661) Boyle published "Some Considerations on the Usefulness of Experimental Natural Philosophy," etc., and in 1663 an extremely interesting paper on "Experiments and Considerations touching Colours." In the course of this paper he describes some very beautiful experiments with a tincture of *Lignum nephriticum*, wherein the dichroism of the extract is made apparent. Boyle found that by transmitted light it appeared of a bright golden colour, but when viewed from the side from which it was illuminated the light emitted was sky blue, and in some cases bright green. By arranging experiments so that some parts of the liquid were seen by the transmitted light and some by the scattered light, very beautiful effects were produced. Boyle endeavoured to learn something of the nature of colours by projecting spectra on differently coloured papers, and observing the appearance of the papers when illuminated by the several spectral rays. He also passed sunlight, concentrated by a lens, through plates of differently coloured glass superposed, allowing the light to fall on a white paper screen, and observing the tint of the light which passed through each combination. But the most interesting of these experiments was the actual mixture of light of different colours by forming two spectra, one by means of a fixed prism, the other by a prism held in the hand, and superposing the latter on the former so that different colours were made to coincide. This experiment was repeated in a modified form, nearly two hundred years later, by Helmholtz, who found that the mixture of blue and yellow lights produced pink. Unfortunately, Boyle's spectra were far from pure, for, the source of light being of considerable dimensions, the different colours overlapped one another, as in Newton's experiments, and in consequence some of his conclusions were inaccurate. Thus blue paper in the yellow part of the spectrum appeared to Boyle green instead of black, but this was due to the admixture of green light with the yellow. He concluded that bodies appear black because they damp the light so as to reflect very little to the eye, but that the surfaces of white bodies consist of innumerable little facets which reflect the light in all directions. In the same year he published some "Observations on a Diamond, which shines in the Dark;" and an extensive treatise on "Some Considerations touching the Style of the Holy Scriptures." Next year appeared several papers from his pen, the most important being "Occasional Reflections upon Several Subjects," the wide scope of which may be gathered from the title. His "New Experiments and Observations touching Cold" were printed in 1665. In this paper he discussed the cause of the force exerted by water in freezing, methods of measuring degrees of cold, the action of freezing-mixtures, and many other questions. He contended that cold was probably only privative, and not a positive existence.

Lord Bacon had asserted that the "essential self" of heat was probably motion and nothing more, and had adduced several experiments and observations in support of this opinion. In his paper on the mechanical origin of heat and cold, Boyle maintained that heat was motion, but motion of the very small particles of bodies, very intense, and taking place in all directions; and that heat could be produced by any means whatever by which the particles of bodies could be agitated. On one occasion he caused two pieces of brass, one convex and the other concave, to be pressed against each other by a spring, and then rubbed together in a vacuum by a rotary motion communicated by a shaft which passed air-tight through the hole in the cover of the receiver, a little emery being inserted between them. In the second experiment the brasses became so hot that he "could not endure to hold [his] hand on either of them." This experiment was intended, like the rubbing of the blocks of ice in vacuo by Davy, to meet the objection that the heat developed by friction was due to the action of the air. The following extract from a paper intended to show that the sense of touch cannot be relied upon for the estimation of temperature, shows that Boyle possessed a very clear insight into the question:—"The account upon which we judge a body to be cold seems to be that we feel its particles less vehemently agitated than those of our fingers or other parts of the organ of touching; and, consequently, if the temper of that organ be changed, the object will appear more or less cold to us, though itself continue of one and the same temperature." To determine the expansion of water in freezing, he filled the bulb and part of the stem of a "bulb tube," or, as it was then generally called, "a philosophical egg," with water, and applying a freezing-mixture, at first to the bottom of the bulb, he succeeded in freezing the water without injury to the glass, and found that 82 volumes of water expanded to 91-1/8 volumes of ice—an expansion of about 11-1/8 per cent. Probably air-bubbles caused the ice to appear to have a greater volume than it really possessed, the true expansion being about nine per cent. of the volume of the water at 4°C. The expansion of water in freezing he employed in order to compress air to a greater extent than he had been able otherwise to compress it. Having nearly filled a tube with water, but left a little air above, and then having sealed the top of the tube, he froze the water from the bottom upwards, so that in expanding it compressed the air to one-tenth of its former volume.

Magnetism and electricity came in for some share of Boyle's attention. He carried out a number of experiments on magnetic induction, and found that lodestones, as well as pieces of iron, when heated and allowed to cool, became magnetized by the induction of the earth. His later experiments with exhausted receivers were not made with his first pump, but with a two-barrelled pump, in which the pistons were connected by a cord passing over a large fixed pulley, so that, when the receiver was nearly exhausted, the pressure of the air on the descending piston during the greater part of the stroke nearly balanced that on the ascending piston. In this respect the pump differed only from Hawksbee's in having the pulley and cord instead of the pinion and two racks. It also resembled Hawksbee's pump in having self-closing valves in the pistons and at the bottom of the cylinders, which, in this pump, had their open ends at the top. The pistons were alternately raised and lowered by the feet of the operator, which were placed in stirrups, of which one was fixed on each piston. The lower portions of the barrels were filled with water, through which the air bubbled, and this, occupying the clearance, enabled a much higher degree of exhaustion to be produced than could be obtained without its employment.

In 1665 Boyle was nominated Provost of Eton, but declined to accept the appointment. His "Hydrostatical Paradoxes," published about this time, contain all the ordinary theorems respecting the pressure of fluids under the action of gravity demonstrated experimentally.

In 1677 Boyle printed, at his own expense, five hundred copies of the four Gospels and the Acts of the Apostles in the Malayan tongue. This was but one of his many contributions towards similar objects.

On November 30, 1680, the Royal Society chose Boyle for President. He, however, declined to accept the appointment, because he had conscientious objections to taking the oath required of the President by the charter of the Society.

It appears that very many of Boyle's manuscripts, which were written in bound books, were taken away, and others mutilated by "corrosive liquors." In May, 1688, he made this known to his friends, but, though these losses put him on his guard, he complained afterwards that all his care and circumspection had not prevented the loss of "six centuries of matters of fact in one parcel," besides many other smaller papers. His works, however, which have been published are so numerous that it would take several pages for the bare enumeration of their titles, many of them being devoted to medical subjects. The edition published in London in 1743 comprises nearly three thousand pages of folio. Boyle always suffered from weak eyes, and in consequence he declined to revise his proofs. In the advertisement to the original edition of his works the publisher mentioned this, and at the same time pleaded his own business engagements as an excuse for not revising the proofs himself! It was partly on account of the injury to his manuscripts, and partly through failing health, that in 1689 he set apart two days in the week, during which he declined to receive visitors, that he might devote himself to his work, and especially to the reparation of the injured writings. About this time he succeeded in procuring the repeal of an Act passed in the fifth year of Henry IV. to the effect "that none from thenceforth should use to multiply gold or silver, or use the craft of multiplication; and if any the same do, they should incur the pain of felony." By this repeal it was made legal to extract gold and silver from ores, or from their mixtures with other metals, in this country provided that the gold and silver so procured should be put to no other use than "the increase of moneys." It is curious that Boyle seems always to have believed in the possibility of transmuting other metals into gold.

His sister, Lady Ranelagh, died on December 23, 1691, and Boyle survived her but a few days, for he died on December 30, and his body was interred near his sister's grave in the chancel of St. Martin's-in-the-Fields. Dr. Shaw, in his preface to Boyle's works, writes, "The men of wit and learning have, in all ages, busied themselves in explaining nature by words; but it is Mr. Boyle alone who has wholly laid himself out in showing philosophy in action. The single point he perpetually keeps in view is to render his reader, not a talkative or a speculative, but an actual and practical philosopher. Himself sets the example; he made all the experiments he possibly could upon natural bodies, and communicated them with all desirable candour and fidelity." The second part of his treatise on "The Christian Virtuoso," Boyle concluded with a number of aphorisms, of which the following well represent his views respecting science:—

"I think it becomes Christian philosophers rather to try whether they can investigate the final causes of things than, without trial, to take it for granted that they are undiscoverable."

"The book of Nature is a fine and large piece of tapestry rolled up, which we are not able to see all at once, but must be content to wait for the discovery of its beauty and symmetry, little by little, as it gradually comes to be more unfolded or displayed."

BENJAMIN FRANKLIN.

Among those whose contributions to physics have immortalized their names in the annals of science, there is none that holds a more prominent position in the history of the world than Benjamin Franklin. At one time a journeyman printer, living in obscure lodgings in London, he became, during the American War of Independence, one of the most conspicuous figures in Europe, and among Americans his reputation was probably second to none, General Washington not excepted.

Professor Laboulaye says of Franklin: "No one ever started from a lower point than the poor apprentice of Boston. No one ever raised himself higher by his own unaided forces than the inventor of the lightning-rod. No one has rendered greater service to his country than the diplomatist who signed the treaty of 1783, and assured the independence of the United States. Better than the biographies of Plutarch, this life, so long and so well filled, is a source of perpetual instruction to all men. Every one can there find counsel and example."

A great part of the history of his life was written by Franklin himself, at first for the edification of the members of his own family, and afterwards at the pressing request of some of his friends in London and Paris. His autobiography does not, however, comprise much more than the first fifty years of his life. The first part was written while he was the guest of the Bishop of St. Asaph, at Twyford; the second portion at Passy, in the house of M. de Chaumont; and the last part in Philadelphia, when he was retiring from public life at the age of eighty-two. The former part of this autobiography was translated into French, and published in Paris, in 1793, though it is not known how the manuscript came into the publisher's hands. The French version was translated into English, and published in England and America, together with such other of Franklin's works as could be collected, before the latter part was given to the world by Franklin's grandson, to whom he had bequeathed his papers, and who first published them in America in 1817.

For a period of three hundred years at least Franklin's family lived on a small freehold of about thirty acres, in the village of Ecton, in Northamptonshire, the eldest son, who inherited the property, being always brought up to the trade of a smith. Franklin himself "was the youngest son of the youngest son for five generations back." His grandfather lived at Ecton till he was too old to follow his business, when he went to live with his second son, John, who was a dyer at Banbury. To this business Franklin's father, Josiah, was apprenticed. The eldest son, Thomas, was brought up a smith, but afterwards

23

became a solicitor; the other son, Benjamin, was a silk-dyer, and followed Josiah to America. He was fond of writing poetry and sermons. The latter he wrote in a shorthand of his own inventing, which he taught to his nephew and namesake, in order that he might utilize the sermons if, as was proposed, he became a Presbyterian minister. Franklin's father, Josiah, took his wife and three children to New England, in 1682, where he practised the trade of a tallow-chandler and soap-boiler. Franklin was born in Boston on January 6 (O.S.), 1706, and was the youngest of seventeen children, of whom thirteen grew up and married.

Benjamin being the youngest of ten sons, his father intended him for the service of the Church, and sent him to the grammar school when eight years of age, where he continued only a year, although he made very rapid progress in the school; for his father concluded that he could not afford the expense of a college education, and at the end of the year removed him to a private commercial school. At the age of ten young Benjamin was taken home to assist in cutting the wicks of candles, and otherwise to make himself useful in his father's business. His enterprising character as a boy is shown by the following story, which is in his own words:—

> There was a salt marsh that bounded part of the mill-pond, on the edge of which, at high-water, we used to stand to fish for minnows. By much trampling we had made it a mere quagmire. My proposal was to build a wharf there fit for us to stand upon, and I showed my comrades a large heap of stones, which were intended for a new house near the marsh, and which would very well suit our purpose. Accordingly, in the evening, when the workmen were gone, I assembled a number of my play-fellows, and working with them diligently, like so many emmets, sometimes two or three to a stone, we brought them all away and built our little wharf. The next morning the workmen were surprised at missing the stones, which were found in our wharf. Inquiry was made after the removers; we were discovered and complained of; several of us were corrected by our fathers; and, though I pleaded the usefulness of the work, mine convinced me that nothing was useful which was not honest.

Until twelve years of age Benjamin continued in his father's business, but as he manifested a great dislike for it, and his parents feared that he might one day run away to sea, they set about finding some trade which would be more congenial to his tastes. With this view his father took him to see various artificers at their work, that he might observe the tastes of the boy. This experience was very valuable to him, as it taught him to do many little jobs for himself when workmen could not readily be procured. During this time Benjamin spent most of his pocket-money in purchasing books, some of which he sold when he had read them, in order to buy others. He read through most of the books in his father's very limited library. These mainly consisted of works on theological controversy, which Franklin afterwards considered to have been not very profitable to him.

"There was another bookish lad in the town, John Collins by name, with whom I was intimately acquainted. We sometimes disputed, and very fond we were of argument, and very desirous of confuting one another, which disputatious turn, by the way, is apt to become a very bad habit, making people often very disagreeable in company by the contradiction that is necessary to bring it into practice; and thence, besides souring and spoiling the conversation, is productive of disgusts and perhaps enmities when you may have occasion for friendship. I had caught it by reading my father's books of dispute about religion. Persons of good sense, I have since observed, seldom fall into it, except lawyers, university men, and men of all sorts that have been bred at Edinburgh."

At length Franklin's fondness for books caused his father to decide to make him a printer. His brother James had already entered that business, and had set up in Boston with a new press and types which he had brought from England. He signed his indentures when only twelve years old, thereby apprenticing himself to his brother until he should attain the age of twenty-one. The acquaintance which he formed with booksellers through the printing business enabled him to borrow a better class of books than he had been accustomed to, and he frequently sat up the greater part of the night to read a book which he had to return in the morning.

While working with his brother, the young apprentice wrote two ballads, which he printed and sold in the streets of Boston. His father, however, ridiculed the performance; so he "escaped being a poet." He adopted at this time a somewhat original method to improve his prose writing. Meeting with an odd volume of the *Spectator*, he purchased it and read it "over and over," and wished to imitate the style. "Making short notes of the sentiment in each sentence," he laid them by, and afterwards tried to write out the papers without looking at the original. Then on comparison he discovered his faults and corrected them. Finding his vocabulary deficient, he turned some of the tales into verse, then retranslated them into prose, believing that the attempt to make verses would necessitate a search for several words of the same meaning. "I also sometimes jumbled my collection of hints into confusion, and after some weeks endeavoured to reduce them into the best order, before I began to form the full sentence and complete the paper. This was to teach me method in the arrangement of my thoughts."

Meeting with a book on vegetarianism, Franklin determined to give the system a trial. This led to some inconvenience in his brother's house-keeping, so Franklin proposed to board himself if his brother would give him half the sum he paid for his board, and out of this he was able to save a considerable amount for the purpose of buying books. Moreover, the time required for meals was so short that the dinner hour afforded considerable leisure for reading. It was on his journey from Boston to Philadelphia that he first violated vegetarian principles; for, a large cod having been caught by the sailors, some small fishes were found in its stomach, whereupon Franklin argued that if fishes ate one another, there could be no reason against eating them, so he dined on cod during the rest of the journey.

After reading Xenophon's "Memorabilia," Franklin took up strongly with the Socratic method of discussion, and became so "artful and expert in drawing people, even of superior knowledge, into concessions, the consequence of which they did not foresee," that some time afterwards one of his employers, before answering the most simple question, would frequently ask what he intended to infer from the answer. This practice he gradually gave up, retaining only the habit of expressing his opinions with "modest diffidence."

In 1720 or 1721 James Franklin began to print a newspaper, the *New England Courant*. To this paper, which he helped to compose and print, Benjamin became an anonymous contributor. The members of the staff spoke highly of his contributions, but when the authorship became known, James appears to have conceived a jealousy of his younger brother, which ultimately led to their separation. An article in the paper having offended the Assembly, James was imprisoned for a month and forbidden to print the paper. He then freed Benjamin from his indentures, in order that the paper might be published in his name. At length, some disagreement arising, Benjamin took advantage of the cancelling of his indentures to quit his brother's service. As he could get no employment in Boston, he obtained a passage to New York, whence he was recommended to go to Philadelphia, which he reached after a very troublesome journey. His whole stock of cash then consisted of a Dutch dollar and about a shilling's worth of coppers. The coppers he gave to the boatmen with whom he came across from Burlington. His first appearance in Philadelphia, about eight o'clock on a Sunday morning, was certainly striking. A youth between seventeen and eighteen years of age, dressed in his working clothes, which were dirty through his journey, with his pockets stuffed out with stockings and shirts, his aspect was not calculated to command respect.

"Then I walked up the street, gazing about till near the market-house I met a boy with bread. I had made many a meal on bread, and, inquiring where he got it, I went immediately to the baker's he directed me to, in Second Street, and ask'd for bisket, intending such as we had in Boston; but they, it seems, were not made in Philadelphia. Then I asked for a threepenny loaf, and was told they had none such. So, not considering or knowing the difference of money, and the greater cheapness, nor the name of his bread, I bad him give me three-penny-worth of any sort. He gave me, accordingly, three great puffy rolls. I was surpriz'd at the quantity, but took it, and having no room in my pockets, walk'd off with a roll under each arm, and eating the other. Thus I went up Market Street as far as Fourth Street, passing by the door of Mr. Read, my future wife's father; when she, standing at the door, saw me, and thought I made, as I certainly did, a most awkward, ridiculous appearance. Then I turned and went down Chestnut Street and part of Walnut Street, eating my roll all the way, and, coming round, found myself again at Market Street Wharf, near the boat I came in, to which I went for a draught of the river water; and, being filled out with one of my rolls, gave the other two to a woman and her child that came down the river in the boat with us, and were waiting to go further."

In Philadelphia Franklin obtained an introduction, through a gentleman he had met at New York, to a printer, named Keimer, who had just set up business with an old press which he appeared not to know how to use, and one pair of cases of English type. Here Franklin obtained employment when the business on hand would permit, and he put the press in order and worked it. Keimer obtained lodgings for him at the house of Mr. Read, and, by industry and economical living, Franklin found himself in easy circumstances. Sir William Keith was then Governor of Pennsylvania, and hearing of Franklin, he called upon him at Keimer's printing-office, invited him to take wine at a neighbouring tavern, and promised to obtain for him the Government printing if he would set up for himself. It was then arranged that Franklin should return to Boston by the first ship, in order to see what help his father would give towards setting him up in business. In the mean while he was frequently invited to dine at the governor's house. Notwithstanding Sir William Keith's recommendation, Josiah Franklin thought his son too young to take the responsibility of a business, and would only promise to assist him if, when he was twenty-one, he had himself saved sufficient to purchase most of the requisite plant. On his return to Philadelphia, he delivered his father's letter to Sir William Keith, whereon the governor, stating that he was determined to have a good printer there, promised to find the means of equipping the printing-office himself, and suggested the desirability of Franklin's making a journey to England in order to purchase the plant. He promised letters of introduction to various persons in England, as well as a letter of credit to furnish the money for the purchase of the printing-plant. These letters Franklin was to call for, but there was always some excuse for their not being ready. At last they were to be sent on board the ship, and Franklin, having gone on board, awaited the letters. When the governor's despatches came, they were all put into a bag together, and the captain promised to let Franklin have his letters before landing. On opening the bag off Plymouth, there were no letters of the kind promised, and Franklin was left without introductions and almost without money, to make his own way in the world. In London he learned that Governor Keith was well known as a man in whom no dependence could be placed, and as to his giving a letter of credit, "he had no credit to give."

A friend of Franklin's, named Ralph, accompanied him from America, and the two took lodgings together in Little Britain at three shillings and sixpence per week. Franklin immediately obtained employment at Palmer's printing-office, in Bartholomew Close; but Ralph, who knew no trade, but aimed at literature, was unable to get any work. He could not obtain employment, even among the law stationers as a copying clerk, so for some time the wages which Franklin earned had to support the two. At Palmer's Franklin was employed in composing Wollaston's "Religion of Nature." On this he wrote a short critique, which he printed. it was entitled "A Dissertation on Liberty and Necessity, Pleasure and Pain." The publication of this he afterwards regretted, but it obtained for him introductions to some literary persons in London. Subsequently he left Palmer's and obtained work at Watts's printing-office, where he remained during the rest of his stay in London. The beer-drinking capabilities of some of his fellow-workmen excited his astonishment. He says:—

> We had an alehouse boy who attended always in the house to supply the workmen. My companion at the press drank every day a pint before breakfast, a pint at breakfast with his bread and cheese, a pint between breakfast and dinner, a pint at dinner, a pint in the afternoon about six o'clock, and another when he had done his day's work. I thought it a detestable custom, but it was necessary, he suppos'd, to drink *strong* beer, that he might be *strong* to labour. I endeavoured to convince him that the bodily strength afforded by beer could only be in proportion to the grain or flour of the barley dissolved in the water of which it was made; that there was more flour in a pennyworth of bread; and therefore, if he would eat that with a pint of water, it would give him more strength than a quart of beer. He drank on, however, and had four or five shillings to pay out of his wages every Saturday night for that muddling liquor; an expense I was free from. And thus these poor devils keep themselves always under.

Afterwards Franklin succeeded in persuading several of the compositors to give up "their muddling breakfast of beer and bread and cheese," for a porringer of hot-water gruel, with pepper, breadcrumbs, and butter, which they obtained from a neighbouring house at a cost of three halfpence.

Among Franklin's fellow-passengers from Philadelphia to England was an American merchant, a Mr. Denham, who had formerly been in business in Bristol, but failed and compounded with his creditors. He then went to America, where he soon acquired a fortune, and returned in Franklin's ship. He invited all his old creditors to dine with him. At the dinner each guest found under his plate a cheque for the balance which had been due to him, with interest to date. This gentleman always remained a firm friend to Franklin, who, during his stay in London, sought his advice when any important questions arose. When Mr. Denham returned to Philadelphia with a quantity of merchandise, he offered Franklin an appointment as clerk, which was afterwards to develop into a commission agency. The offer was accepted, and, after a voyage of nearly three months, Franklin reached Philadelphia on October 11, 1726. Here he found Governor Keith had been superseded by Major Gordon, and, what was of more importance to him, that Miss Read, to whom he had become engaged before leaving for England, and to whom he had written only once during his absence, had married. Shortly after starting in business, Mr. Denham died, and thus left Franklin to commence life again for himself. Keimer had by this time obtained a fairly extensive establishment, and employed a number of hands, but none of them were of much value; and he made overtures to Franklin to take the management of his printing-office, apparently with the intention of getting his men taught their business, so that he might afterwards be able to dispense with the manager. Franklin set the printing-house in order, started type-founding, made the ink, and, when necessary, executed engravings. As the other hands improved under his superintendence, Keimer began to treat his manager less civilly, and apparently desired to curtail his stipend. At length, through an outbreak of temper on the part of Keimer, Franklin left, but was afterwards induced to return in order to prepare copper-plates and a press for printing paper money for New Jersey.

While working for Keimer, Franklin formed a club, which was destined to exert considerable influence on American politics. The club met on Friday evenings, and was called the Junto. It was essentially a debating society, the subject for each evening's discussion being proposed at the preceding meeting. One of the rules was that the existence of the club should remain a secret, and that its members should be limited to twelve. Afterwards other similar clubs were formed by its members; but the existence of the Junto was kept a secret from them. The club lasted for about forty years, and became the nucleus of the American Philosophical Society, of which Franklin was the first president. This, and the fact that many of the great questions that arose previously to the Declaration of Independence were discussed in the Junto in the first instance, give to the club a special importance. The following are specimens of subjects discussed by the club:—

"Is sound an entity or body?"

"How may the phenomena of vapours be explained?"

"Is self-interest the rudder that steers mankind, the universal monarch to whom all are tributaries?"

"Which is the best form of government? and what was that form which first prevailed among mankind?"

"Can any one particular form of government suit all mankind?"

"What is the reason that the tides rise higher in the Bay of Fundy than the Bay of Delaware?"

"Is the emission of paper money safe?"

"What is the reason that men of the greatest knowledge are not the most happy?"

"How may the possessions of the Lakes be improved to our advantage?"

"Why are tumultuous, uneasy sensations united with our desires?"

"Whether it ought to be the aim of philosophy to eradicate the passions."

"How may smoky chimneys be best cured?"

"Why does the flame of a candle tend upwards in a spire?"

"Which is least criminal—a bad action joined with a good intention, or a good action with a bad intention?"

"Is it consistent with the principles of liberty in a free government to punish a man as a libeller when he speaks the truth?"

On leaving Keimer's, Franklin went into partnership with one of his fellow-workmen, Hugh Meredith, whose father found the necessary capital, and a printing-office was started which soon excelled its two rivals in Philadelphia. Franklin's industry attracted the attention of the townsfolk, and inspired the merchants with confidence in the prospects of the new concern. Keimer started a newspaper, which he had not the ability to carry on; Franklin purchased it from him for a trifle, remodelled it, and continued it in a very spirited manner under the title of the *Pennsylvania Gazette*. His political articles soon attracted the attention of the principal men of the state; the number of subscribers increased rapidly, and the paper became a source of considerable profit. Soon after, the printing for the House of Representatives came into the hands of the firm. Meredith never took to the business, and was seldom sober, and at length was bought out by his partner, on July 14, 1730. The discussion in the Junto on paper currency induced Franklin to publish a paper entitled "The Nature and Necessity of a Paper Currency." This was a prominent subject before the House, but the introduction of paper money was opposed by the capitalists. They were unable, however, to answer Franklin's arguments; the point was carried in the House, and Franklin was employed to print the money. The amount of paper money in Pennsylvania in 1739 amounted to £80,000; during the war it rose to more than £350,000.

"In order to secure my credit and character as a tradesman, I took care not only to be in *reality* industrious and frugal, but to avoid all appearances to the contrary. I drest plainly; I was seen at no places of idle diversion. I never went out a-fishing or shooting; a book, indeed, sometimes debauch'd me from my work, but that was seldom, snug, and gave no scandal; and, to show that I was not above my business, I sometimes brought home the paper I purchas'd at the stores thro' the streets on a wheelbarrow. Thus being esteem'd an industrious, thriving young man, and paying duly for what I bought, the merchants who imported stationery solicited my custom; others proposed supplying me with books, and I went on swimmingly. In the mean time, Keimer's credit and business declining daily, he was at last forc'd to sell his printing-house to satisfy his creditors."

On September 1, 1730, Franklin married his former *fiancée*, whose previous husband had left her and was reported to have died in the West Indies. The marriage was a very happy one, and continued over forty years, Mrs. Franklin living until the end of 1774. Industry and frugality reigned in the household of the young printer. Mrs. Franklin not only managed the house, but assisted in the business, folding and stitching pamphlets, and in other ways making herself useful. The first part of Franklin's autobiography concludes with an account of the foundation of the first subscription library. By the co-operation of the members of the Junto, fifty subscribers were obtained, who each paid in the first instance forty shillings, and afterwards ten shillings per annum. "We afterwards obtained a charter, the company being increased to one hundred. This was the mother of all the North American subscription libraries, now so numerous. It is become a great thing itself, and continually increasing. These libraries have improved the general conversation of the Americans, made the common tradesmen and farmers as intelligent as most gentlemen from other countries, and perhaps have contributed in some degree to the stand so generally made throughout the colonies in defence of their privileges."

Ten years ago this library contained between seventy and eighty thousand volumes.

Franklin's success in business was attributed by him largely to his early training. "My circumstances, however, grew daily easier. My original habits of frugality continuing, and my father having, among his instructions to me when a boy, frequently repeated a proverb of Solomon, 'Seest thou a man diligent in his business? he shall stand before kings; he shall not stand before mean men,' I from thence considered industry as a means of obtaining wealth and distinction, which encourag'd me, tho' I did not think that I should ever literally *stand before kings*, which, however, has since happened; for I have stood before *five*, and even had the honour of sitting down with one, the King of Denmark, to dinner."

After his marriage, Franklin conceived the idea of obtaining moral perfection. He was not altogether satisfied with the result, but thought his method worthy of imitation. Assuming that he possessed complete knowledge of what was right or wrong, he saw no reason why he should not always act in accordance therewith. His principle was to devote his attention to one virtue only at first for a week, at the end of which time he expected the practice of that virtue to have become a habit. He then added another virtue to his list, and devoted his attention to the same for the next week, and so on, until he had exhausted his list of virtues. He then commenced again at the beginning. As his moral code comprised thirteen virtues, it was possible to go through the complete curriculum four times in a year. Afterwards he occupied a year in going once through the list, and subsequently employed several years in one course. A little book was ruled, with a column for each day and a line for each virtue, and in this a mark was made for every failure which could be remembered on examination at the end of the day. It is easy to believe his statement: "I am surprised to find myself so much fuller of faults than I had imagined; but I had the satisfaction of seeing them diminish."

"This my little book had for its motto these lines from Addison's 'Cato':—

"'Here will I hold. If there's a Power above us
(And that there is, all Nature cries aloud
Thro' all her work), He must delight in virtue;
And that which He delights in must be happy.'

"Another from Cicero:—

"'O vitæ Philosophia dux! O virtutum indagatrix expultrixque vitiorum! Unus dies ex præceptis tuis actus, peccanti immortalitati est anteponendus.'

"Another from the Proverbs of Solomon, speaking of wisdom and virtue:—

"'Length of days is in her right hand; and in her left hand riches and honour. Her ways are ways of pleasantness, and all her paths are peace.'

"And conceiving God to be the fountain of wisdom, I thought it right and necessary to solicit His assistance for obtaining it; to this end I formed the following little prayer, which was prefixed to my tables of examination, for daily use:—

"'O powerful Goodness! bountiful Father! merciful Guide! increase in me that wisdom which discovers my truest interest. Strengthen my resolutions to perform what that wisdom dictates. Accept my kind offices to Thy other children as the only return in my power for Thy continual favours to me.'

"I used also sometimes a little prayer which I took from Thomson's Poems, viz.:—

"'Father of light and life, Thou Good Supreme!
Oh teach me what is good; teach me Thyself!
Save me from folly, vanity, and vice,
From every low pursuit; and fill my soul
With knowledge, conscious peace, and virtue pure;
Sacred, substantial, never-failing bliss!'"

The senses in which Franklin's thirteen virtues were to be understood were explained by short precepts which followed them in his list. The list was as follows:—

"1. TEMPERANCE.

"Eat not to dulness; drink not to elevation.

"2. SILENCE.

"Speak not but what may benefit others or yourself; avoid trifling conversation.

"3. ORDER.

"Let all your things have their places; let each part of your business have its time.

"Resolve to perform what you ought; perform without fail what you resolve.

"5. Frugality.

"Make no expense but to do good to others or yourself; *i.e.* waste nothing.

"6. Industry.

"Lose no time; be always employed in something useful; cut off all unnecessary actions.

"7. Sincerity.

"Use no hurtful deceit; think innocently and justly; and, if you speak, speak accordingly.

"8. Justice.

"Wrong none by doing injuries, or omitting the benefits that are your duty.

"9. Moderation.

"Avoid extremes; forbear resenting injuries so much as you think they deserve.

"10. Cleanliness.

"Tolerate no uncleanness in body, clothes, or habitation.

"11. Tranquillity.

"Be not disturbed at trifles, or accidents common or unavoidable.

"12. Chastity.

"13. Humility.

"Imitate Jesus and Socrates."

The last of these was added to the list at the suggestion of a Quaker friend. Franklin claims to have acquired a good deal of the *appearance* of it, but concluded that in reality there was no passion so hard to subdue as *pride*. "For even if I could conceive that I had completely overcome it, I should probably be proud of my humility." The virtue which gave him most trouble, however, was order, and this he never acquired.

In 1732 appeared the first copy of "Poor Richard's Almanack." This was prepared, printed, and published by Franklin for about twenty-five years in succession, and nearly ten thousand copies were sold annually. Besides the usual astronomical information, it contained a collection of entertaining anecdotes, verses, jests, etc., while the "little spaces that occurred between the remarkable events in the calendar" were filled with proverbial sayings, inculcating industry and frugality as helps to virtue. These sayings were collected and prefixed to the almanack of 1757, whence they were copied into the American newspapers, and afterwards reprinted as a broad-sheet in England and in France.

In 1733 Franklin commenced studying modern languages, and acquired sufficient knowledge of French, Italian, and Spanish to be able to read books in those languages. In 1736 he was chosen Clerk to the General Assembly, an office to which he was annually re-elected until he became a member of the Assembly about 1750. There was one member who, on the second occasion of his election, made a long speech against him. Franklin determined to secure the friendship of this member. Accordingly he wrote to him to request the loan of a very scarce and curious book which was in his library. The book was lent and returned in about a week, with a note of thanks. The member ever after manifested a readiness to serve Franklin, and they became great friends—"Another instance of the truth of an old maxim I had learned, which says, *'He that has once done you a kindness will be more ready to do you another than he whom you yourself have obliged.'* And it shows how much more profitable it is prudently to remove, than to resent, return, and continue inimical proceedings."

In 1737 Franklin was appointed Deputy-Postmaster-General for Pennsylvania. He was afterwards made Postmaster-General of the Colonies. He read a paper in the Junto on the organization of the City watch, and the propriety of rating the inhabitants on the value of their premises in order to support the same. The subject was also discussed in the other clubs which had sprung from the Junto, and thus the way was prepared for the law which a few years afterwards carried Franklin's proposals into effect. His next scheme was the formation of a fire brigade, in which he met with his usual success, and other clubs followed, until most of the men of property in the city were members of one club or another. The original brigade, known as the Union Fire Company, was formed December 7, 1736. It was in active service in 1791.

Franklin founded the American Philosophical Society in 1743. The headquarters of the society were fixed in Philadelphia, where it was arranged that there should always be at least seven members, viz. a physician, a botanist, a mathematician, a chemist, a mechanician, a geographer, and a general natural philosopher, besides a president, treasurer, and secretary. The other members might be resident in any part of America. Correspondence was to be kept up with the Royal Society of London and the Dublin Society, and abstracts of the communications were to be sent quarterly to all the members. Franklin became the first secretary.

Spain, having been for some years at war with England, was joined at length by France. This threatened danger to the American colonies, as France then held Canada, and no organization for their defence existed. Franklin published a pamphlet entitled "Plain Truth," setting forth the unarmed condition of the colonies, and recommending the formation of a volunteer force for defensive purposes. The pamphlet excited much attention. A public meeting was held and addressed by Franklin; at this meeting twelve hundred joined the association. At length the number of members enrolled exceeded ten thousand. These all provided themselves with arms, formed regiments and companies, elected their own officers, and attended once a week for military drill. Franklin was elected colonel of the Philadelphia Regiment, but declined the appointment, and served as a private soldier. The provision of war material was a difficulty with the Assembly, which consisted largely of Quakers, who, though they appeared privately to be willing that the country should be put in a state of defence, hesitated to vote in opposition to their peace principles. Hence it was that, when the Government of New England asked a grant of gunpowder from Pennsylvania, the Assembly voted £3000 "for the purchasing of bread, flour, wheat, or *other grain*." Pebble-powder was not then in use. When it was proposed to devote £60, which was a balance in the hands of the Union Fire Company, as a contribution towards the erection of a battery below the town, Franklin suggested that it should be proposed that a fire-engine be purchased with the money, and that the committee should "buy a great gun, which is certainly a *fire-engine*."

The "Pennsylvania fireplace" was invented in 1742. A patent was offered to Franklin by the Governor of Pennsylvania, but he declined it on the principle *"that, as we enjoy great advantages from the inventions of others, we should be glad of an opportunity to serve others by any invention of ours; and this we should do freely and generously."* An ironmonger in London made slight alterations, which were not improvements, in the design, and took out a patent for the fireplace, whereby he made a "small fortune." Franklin never contested the patent, "having no desire of profiting by patents himself," and "hating disputes." This fireplace was designed to burn wood, but, unlike the German stoves, it was completely open in front, though enclosed at the sides and top. An air-chamber was formed in the middle of the stove, so arranged that, while the burning wood was in contact with the front of the chamber, the flame passed above and behind it on its way to the flue. Through this chamber a constant current of air passed, entering the room heated, but not contaminated, by the products of combustion. In this way the stove furnished a constant supply of fresh warm air to the room, while it possessed all the advantages of an open fireplace. Subsequently Franklin contrived a special fireplace for the combustion of coal. In the scientific thought which he devoted to the requirements of the domestic economist, as in very many other particulars, Franklin strongly reminds us of Count Rumford.

The next important enterprise which Franklin undertook, partly through the medium of the Junto, was to establish an academy which soon developed into the University of Philadelphia. The members of the club having taken up the subject, the next step was to enlist the sympathy of a wider constituency, and this Franklin effected, in his usual way, by the publication of a pamphlet. He then set on foot a subscription, the payments to extend over five years, and thereby obtained about £5000. A house was taken and schools opened in 1749. The classes soon became too large for the house, and the trustees of the academy then took over a large building, or "tabernacle," which had been erected for George Whitefield when he was preaching in Philadelphia. The hall was divided into stories, and at a very small expense adapted to the requirements of the classes. Franklin, having taken a partner in his printing business, took the oversight of the work. Afterwards the funds were increased by English subscriptions, by a grant from the Assembly, and by gifts of land from the proprietaries; and thus was established the University of Philadelphia.

Having practically retired from business, Franklin intended to devote himself to philosophical studies, having commenced his electrical researches some time before in conjunction with the other members of the Library Company. Public business, however, crowded upon him. He was elected a member of the Assembly, a councillor and afterwards an alderman of the city, and by the governor was made a justice of the peace. As a member of the Assembly, he was largely concerned in providing the means for the erection of a hospital, and in arranging for the paving and cleansing of the streets of the city. In 1753 he was appointed, in conjunction with Mr. Hunter, Postmaster-General of America. The post-office of the colonies had previously been conducted at a loss. In a few years, under Franklin's management, it not only paid the stipends of himself and Mr. Hunter, but yielded a considerable revenue to the Crown. But it was not only in the conduct of public business that Franklin's merits were recognized. By this time he had secured his reputation as an electrician, and both Yale College and Cambridge University (New England) conferred on him the honorary degree of Master of Arts. In the same year that he was made Postmaster-General of America he was awarded the Copley Medal and elected a Fellow of the Royal Society of London, the usual fees being remitted in his case.

Before his election as member, Franklin had for several years held the appointment of Clerk to the Assembly, and he used to relieve the dulness of the debates by amusing himself in the construction of magic circles and squares, and "acquired such a knack at it" that he could "fill the cells of any magic square of reasonable size with a series of numbers as fast as" he "could write them." Many years afterwards Mr. Logan showed Franklin a French folio volume filled with magic squares, and afterwards a magic "square of 16," which Mr. Logan thought must have been a work of great labour, though it possessed only the common properties of making 2056 in every row, horizontal, vertical, and diagonal. During the evening Franklin made the square shown on the opposite page. "This I sent to our friend the next morning, who, after some days, sent it back in a letter, with these words: 'I return to thee thy astonishing and most stupendous piece of the magical square, in which——;' but the compliment is too extravagant, and therefore, for his sake as well as my own, I ought not to repeat it. Nor is it necessary; for I make no question that you will readily allow this square of 16 to be the most magically magical of any magic square ever made by any magician."

The square has the following properties:—Every straight row of sixteen numbers, whether vertical, horizontal, or diagonal, makes 2056.

Every bent row of sixteen numbers, as shown by the diagonal lines in the figure, makes 2056.

If a square hole be cut in a piece of paper, so as to show through it just sixteen of the little squares, and the paper be laid on the magic square, then, wherever the paper is placed, the sum of the sixteen numbers visible through the hole will be 2056.

200	217	232	249	8	25	40	57	72	89	104	121	136	153	168	185
58	39	26	7	250	231	218	199	186	167	154	135	122	103	90	71
198	219	230	251	6	27	38	59	70	91	102	123	134	155	166	187
60	37	28	5	252	229	220	197	188	165	156	133	124	101	92	69
201	216	233	248	9	24	41	56	73	88	105	120	137	152	169	184
55	42	23	10	247	234	215	202	183	170	151	138	119	106	87	74
203	214	235	246	11	22	43	54	75	86	107	118	139	150	171	182
53	44	21	12	245	236	213	204	181	172	149	140	117	108	85	76
205	212	237	244	13	20	45	52	77	84	109	116	141	148	173	180
51	46	19	14	243	238	211	206	179	174	147	142	115	110	83	78
207	210	239	242	15	18	47	50	79	82	111	114	143	146	175	178
49	48	17	16	241	240	209	208	177	176	145	144	113	112	81	80
196	221	228	253	4	29	36	61	68	93	100	125	132	157	164	189
62	35	30	3	254	227	222	195	190	163	158	131	126	99	94	67

194	223	226	255	2	31	34	63	66	95	98	127	130	159	162	191
64	33	32	1	256	225	224	193	192	161	160	129	128	97	96	65

In 1754 war with France appeared to be again imminent, and a Congress of Commissioners from the several colonies was arranged for. Of course, Franklin was one of the representatives of Pennsylvania, and was also one of the members who independently drew up a plan for the union of all the colonies under one government, for defensive and other general purposes, and his was the plan finally approved by Congress for the union, though it was not accepted by the Assemblies or by the English Government, being regarded by the former as having too much of the *prerogative* in it, by the latter as being too *democratic*. Franklin wrote respecting this scheme: "The different and contrary reasons of dislike to my plan makes me suspect that it was really the true medium; and I am still of opinion that it would have been happy for both sides of the water if it had been adopted. The colonies, so united, would have been sufficiently strong to have defended themselves; there would then have been no need of troops from England; of course, the subsequent pretence for taxing America, and the bloody contest it occasioned, would have been avoided."

With this war against France began the struggle of the Assemblies and the proprietaries on the question of taxing the estates of the latter. The governors received strict instructions to approve no bills for the raising of money for the purposes of defence, unless the estates of the proprietaries were specially exempted from the tax. The Assembly of Pennsylvania resolved to contribute £10,000 to assist the Government of Massachusetts Bay in an attack upon Crown Point, but the governor refused his assent to the bill for raising the money. At this juncture Franklin proposed a scheme by which the money could be raised without the consent of the governor. His plan was successful, and the difficulty was surmounted for the time, but was destined to recur again and again during the progress of the war.

The British Government, not approving of the scheme of union, whereby the colonies might have defended themselves, sent General Braddock to Virginia, with two regiments of regular troops. On their arrival they found it impossible to obtain waggons for the conveyance of their baggage, and the general commissioned Franklin to provide them in Pennsylvania. By giving his private bond for their safety, Franklin succeeded in engaging one hundred and fifty four-horse waggons, and two hundred and fifty-nine pack-horses. His modest warnings against Indian ambuscades were disregarded by the general, the little army was cut to pieces, and the remainder took to flight, sacrificing the whole of their baggage and stores. Franklin was never fully recouped by the British Government for the payments he had to make on account of provisions which the general had instructed him to procure for the use of the army.

After this, Franklin appeared for some time in a purely military capacity, having yielded to the governor's persuasions to undertake the defence of the north-western frontier, to raise troops, and to build a line of forts. After building and manning three wooden forts, he was recalled by the Assembly, whose relations with the governor had become more and more strained. At length the Assembly determined to send Franklin to England, to present a petition to the king respecting the conduct of the proprietaries, viz. Richard and Thomas Penn, the successors of William Penn. A bill had been framed by the House to provide £60,000 for the king's use in the defence of the province. This the governor refused to pass, because the proprietary estates were not exempted from the taxation. The petition to the king was drawn up, and Franklin's baggage was on board the ship which was to convey him to England, when General Lord Loudon endeavoured to make an arrangement between the parties. The governor pleaded his instructions, and the bond he had given for carrying them out, and the Assembly was prevailed upon to reconstruct the bill in accordance with the governor's wishes. This was done under protest; in the mean time Franklin's ship had sailed, carrying his baggage. After a great deal of unnecessary delay on account of the general's inability to decide upon the despatch of the packet-boats, Franklin at last got away from New York, and, having narrowly escaped shipwreck off Falmouth, he reached London on July 27, 1757.

On arriving in London, Franklin was introduced to Lord Granville, who told him that the king's instructions were laws in the colonies. Franklin replied that he had always understood that the Assemblies made the laws, which then only required the king's consent. "I recollected that, about twenty years before, a clause in a bill brought into Parliament by the Ministry had proposed to make the king's instructions laws in the colonies, but the clause was thrown out by the Commons, for which we adored them as our friends and the friends of liberty, till, by their conduct towards us in 1765, it seem'd that they had refus'd that point of sovereignty to the king only that they might reserve it for themselves." A meeting was shortly afterwards arranged between Franklin and the proprietaries at Mr. T. Penn's house; but their views were so discordant that, after some discussion, Franklin was requested to give them in writing the heads of his complaints, and the whole question was submitted to the opinion of the attorney- and solicitor-general. It was nearly a year before this opinion was given. The proprietaries then communicated directly with the Assembly, but in the mean while Governor Denny had consented to a bill for raising £100,000 for the king's use, in which it was provided that the proprietary estates should be taxed with the others. When this bill reached

England, the proprietaries determined to oppose its receiving the royal assent. Franklin engaged counsel on behalf of the Assembly, and on his undertaking that the assessment should be fairly made between the estates of the proprietaries and others, the bill was allowed to pass.

By this time Franklin's career as a scientific investigator was practically at an end. Political business almost completely occupied his attention, and in one sense the diplomatist replaced the philosopher. His public scientific career was of short duration. It may be said to have begun in 1746, when Mr. Peter Collinson presented an "electrical tube" to the Library Company in Philadelphia, which was some time after followed by a present of a complete set of electrical apparatus from the proprietaries, but by 1755 Franklin's time was so much taken up by public business that there was very little opportunity for experimental work. Throughout his life he frequently expressed in his letters his strong desire to return to philosophy, but the opportunity never came, and when, at the age of eighty-two, he was liberated from public duty, his strength was insufficient to enable him to complete even his autobiography.

It was on a visit to Boston in 1746 that Franklin met with Dr. Spence, a Scotchman, who exhibited some electrical experiments. Soon after his return to Philadelphia the tube arrived from Mr. Collinson, and Franklin acquired considerable dexterity in its use. His house was continually full of visitors, who came to see the experiments, and, to relieve the pressure upon his time, he had a number of similar tubes blown at the glass-house, and these he distributed to his friends, so that there were soon a number of "performers" in Philadelphia. One of these was Mr. Kinnersley, who, having no other employment, was induced by Franklin to become an itinerant lecturer. Franklin drew up a scheme for the lectures, and Kinnersley obtained several well-constructed instruments from Franklin's rough and home-made models. Kinnersley and Franklin appear to have worked together a good deal, and when Kinnersley was travelling on his lecture tour, each communicated to the other the results of his experiments. Franklin sent his papers to Mr. Collinson, who presented them to the Royal Society, but they were not at first judged worthy of a place in the "Transactions." The paper on the identity of lightning and electricity was sent to Dr. Mitchell, who read it before the Royal Society, when it "was laughed at by the connoisseurs." The papers were subsequently published in a pamphlet, but did not at first receive much attention in England. On the recommendation of Count de Buffon, they were translated into French. The Abbé Nollet, who had previously published a theory of his own respecting electricity, wrote and published a volume of letters defending his theory, and denying the accuracy of some of Franklin's experimental results. To these letters Franklin made no reply, but they were answered by M.

le Roy. M. de Lor undertook to repeat in Paris all Franklin's experiments, and they were performed before the king and court. Not content with the experiments which Franklin had actually performed, he tried those which had been only suggested, and so was the first to obtain electricity from the clouds by means of the pointed rod. This experiment produced a great sensation everywhere, and was afterwards repeated by Franklin at Philadelphia. Franklin's papers were translated into Italian, German, and Latin; his theory met with all but universal acceptance, and great surprise was expressed that his papers had excited so little interest in England. Dr. Watson then drew up a summary of all Franklin's papers, and this was published in the "Philosophical Transactions;" Mr. Canton verified the experiment of procuring electricity from the clouds by means of a pointed rod, and the Royal Society awarded to Franklin the Copley Medal for 1753, which was conveyed to him by Governor Denny.

We must now give a short account of Franklin's contributions to electrical science.

"The first is the wonderful effect of pointed bodies, both in *drawing off* and *throwing off* the electrical fire."

It will be observed that this statement is made in the language of the *one*-fluid theory, of which Franklin may be regarded as the author. This theory will be again referred to presently. Franklin electrified a cannon-ball so that it repelled a cork. On bringing near it the point of a bodkin, the repulsion disappeared. A blunt body had to be brought near enough for a spark to pass in order to produce the same effect. "To prove that the electrical fire is *drawn off* by the point, if you take the blade of the bodkin out of the wooden handle, and fix it in a stick of sealing-wax, and then present it at the distance aforesaid, or if you bring it very near, no such effect follows; but sliding one finger along the wax till you touch the blade, and the ball flies to the shot immediately. If you present the point in the dark, you will see, sometimes at a foot distance or more, a light gather upon it like that of a fire-fly or glow-worm; the less sharp the point, the nearer you must bring it to observe the light; and at whatever distance you see the light, you may draw off the electrical fire, and destroy the repelling."

By laying a needle upon the shot, Franklin showed "that points will *throw off* as well as *draw off* the electrical fire." A candle-flame was found to be equally efficient with a sharp point in drawing off the electricity from a charged conductor. The effect of the candle-flame Franklin accounted for by supposing the particles separated from the candle to be first "attracted and then repelled, carrying off the electric matter with them." The effect of points is a direct consequence of the law of electrical repulsion. When a conductor is electrified, the density of the electricity is greatest where the curvature is greatest. Thus, if a number of spheres are electrified from the same source, the density of the electricity on the different spheres will vary inversely as their diameters. The force tending to drive the electricity off a conductor is everywhere proportional to the density, and hence in the case of the spheres will be greatest for the smallest sphere. On this principle, the density of electricity on a perfectly sharp point, if such could exist, on a charged conductor, would be infinite and the force tending to drive it off would be infinite also. Hence a moderately sharp point is sufficient to dissipate the electricity from a highly charged conductor, or to neutralize it if the point is connected to earth and brought near the conductor so as to be electrified by induction.

Franklin next found that, if the person rubbing the electric tube stood upon a cake of resin, and the person taking the charge from the tube stood also on an insulating stand, a stronger spark would pass between these two persons than between either of them and the earth; that, after the spark had passed, neither person was electrified, though each had appeared electrified before. These experiments suggested the idea of *positive* and *negative* electrification; and Franklin, regarding the electric fluid as corresponding to positive electrification, remarked that "you may circulate it as Mr. Watson has shown; you may also accumulate or subtract it upon or from any body, as you connect that body with the rubber or with the receiver, the common stock being cut off." Thus Franklin regarded electricity as a fluid, of which everything in its normal state possesses a certain amount; that, by appropriate means, some of the fluid may be removed from one body and given to another. The former is then electrified negatively, the latter positively, and all processes by which bodies are electrified consist in the removal of electricity from one body or system and giving it to another. He regarded the electric fluid as repelling itself and attracting matter. Æpinus afterwards added the supposition that matter, when devoid of electricity, is self-repulsive, and thus completed the "one-fluid theory," and accounted for the repulsion observed between negatively electrified bodies.

It had been usual to employ water for the interior armatures of Leyden jars, or phials, as they were then generally called. Franklin substituted granulated lead for the water, thereby improving the insulation by keeping the glass dry. With these phials he contrived many ingenious experiments, and imitated lightning by discharging them through the gilding of a mirror or the gold lines on the cover of a book. He found that the inner and outer armatures of his Leyden jars were oppositely electrified. "Here we have a bottle containing at the same time a *plenum* of electrical fire and a *vacuum* of the same fire; and yet the equilibrium cannot be restored between them but by a communication *without!* though the plenum presses violently to expand, and the hungry vacuum seems to attract as violently in order to be filled." The charging of Leyden jars by cascade, that is by insulating all the jars except the last, connecting the outer armature of the first with the inner armature of the second, and so on throughout the series, was well understood by Franklin, and he knew too that by this method the extent to which each jar could be charged from a given source varied inversely as the number of jars. The discharge of the Leyden jar by alternate contacts was also carried out by him; and he found that, if the jar is first placed on an insulating stand, it may be held by the hook (or knob) without discharging it. Franklin, in fact, appears to have known almost as much about the Leyden jar as is known to-day. He found that, when the armatures were removed from a jar, no discharge would pass between them, but when a fresh pair of armatures were supplied to the glass, the jar could be discharged. "We are of opinion that there is really no more electrical fire in the phial after what is called its *charging* than before, nor less after its *discharging*; excepting only the small spark that might be given to and taken from the non-electric matter, if separated from the bottle, which spark may not be equal to a five-hundredth part of what is called the explosion.

"The phial will not suffer what is called a *charging* unless as much fire can go out of it one way as is thrown in by another.

"When a bottle is charged in the common way, its *inside* and *outside* surfaces stand ready, the one to give fire by the hook, the other to receive it by the coating; the one is full and ready to throw out, the other empty and extremely hungry; yet, as the first will not *give out* unless the other can at the same time *receive in*, so neither will the latter receive in unless the first can at the same time give out. When both can be done at once, it is done with inconceivable quickness and violence."

Then follows a very beautiful illustration of the condition of the glass in the Leyden jar.

"So a straight spring (though the comparison does not agree in every particular), when forcibly bent, must, to restore itself, contract that side which in the bending was extended, and extend that which was contracted; if either of these two operations be hindered, the other cannot be done.

"Glass, in like manner, has, within its substance, always the same quantity of electrical fire, and that a very great quantity in proportion to the mass of the glass, as shall be shown hereafter.

"This quantity proportioned to the glass it strongly and obstinately retains, and will have neither more nor less, though it will suffer a change to be made in its parts and situation; *i.e.* we may take away part of it from one of the sides, provided we throw an equal quantity into the other."

"The whole force of the bottle, and power of giving a shock, is in the GLASS ITSELF; the non-electrics in contact with the two surfaces serving only to *give* and *receive* to and from the several parts of the glass, that is, to give on one side and take away from the other."

All these statements were, as far as possible, fully substantiated by experiment. They are perfectly consistent with the views held by Cavendish and by Clerk Maxwell, and, though the phraseology is not that of the modern text-books, the statements themselves can hardly be improved upon to-day.

One of Franklin's early contrivances was an electro-motor, which was driven by the alternate electrical attraction and repulsion of leaden bullets which discharged Leyden jars by alternate contacts. Franklin concluded his account of these experiments as follows:—

> Chagrined a little that we have been hitherto able to produce nothing in this way of use to mankind, and the hot weather coming on, when electrical experiments are not so agreeable, it is proposed to put an end to them for this season, somewhat humorously, in a party of pleasure, on the banks of Skuylkil. Spirits, at the same time, are to be fired by a spark sent from side to side through the river, without any other conductor than the water—an experiment which we some time since performed, to the amazement of many. A turkey is to be killed for our dinner by the *electrical shock*, and roasted by the *electrical jack* before a fire kindled by the *electrified bottle*, when the healths of all the famous electricians in England, Holland, France, and Germany, are to be drunk in *electrified bumpers*, under the discharge of guns from the *electrical battery*.

Franklin's electrical battery consisted of eleven large panes of glass coated on each side with sheet lead. The electrified bumper was a thin tumbler nearly filled with wine and electrified as a Leyden jar, so as to give a shock through the lips.

Franklin's theory of the manner in which thunder-clouds become electrified he found to be not consistent with his subsequent experiments. In the paper which he wrote explaining this theory, however, he shows some knowledge of the effects of bringing conductors into contact in diminishing their capacity. He states that two gun-barrels electrified equally and then united, will give a spark at a greater distance than one alone. Hence he asks, "To what a great distance may ten thousand acres of electrified cloud strike and give its fire, and how loud must be that crack?

"An electrical spark, drawn from an irregular body at some distance, is scarcely ever straight, but shows crooked and waving in the air. So do the flashes of lightning, the clouds being very irregular bodies.

"As electrified clouds pass over a country, high hills and high trees, lofty towers, spires, masts of ships, chimneys, etc., as so many prominences and points, draw the electrical fire, and the whole cloud discharges there.

"Dangerous, therefore, is it to take shelter under a tree during a thunder-gust. It has been fatal to many, both men and beasts.

"It is safer to be in the open field for another reason. When the clothes are wet, if a flash in its way to the ground should strike your head, it may run in the water over the surface of your body; whereas, if your clothes were dry, it would go through the body, because the blood and other humours, containing so much water, are more ready conductors.

"Hence a wet rat cannot be killed by the exploding electrical bottle [a quart jar], while a dry rat may."

In the above quotations we see, so to speak, the germ of the lightning-rod. This was developed in a letter addressed to Mr. Collinson, and dated July 29, 1750. The following quotations will give an idea of its contents:—

"The electrical matter consists of particles extremely subtile, since it can permeate common matter, even the densest metals, with such ease and freedom as not to receive any perceptible resistance.[1]

[1] Franklin was aware of the resistance of conductors (see p. 96).

"If any one should doubt whether the electrical matter passes through the substance of bodies or only over and along their surfaces, a shock from an electrified large glass jar, taken through his own body, will probably convince him.

"Common matter is a kind of sponge to the electrical fluid.

"We know that the electrical fluid is *in* common matter, because we can pump it *out* by the globe or tube. We know that common matter has near as much as it can contain, because when we add a little more to any portion of it, the additional quantity does not enter, but forms an electrical atmosphere."

To illustrate the action of a lightning-conductor on a thunder-cloud, Franklin suspended from the ceiling a pair of scales by a twisted string so that the beam revolved. Upon the floor, in such a position that the scale-pans passed over it, he placed a blunt steel punch. The scale-pans were suspended by silk threads, and one of them electrified. When this passed over the punch it dipped towards it, and sometimes discharged into it by a spark. When a needle was placed with its point uppermost by the side of the punch, no attraction was apparent, for the needle discharged the scale-pan before it came near.

"Now, if the fire of electricity and that of lightning be the same, as I have endeavoured to show at large in a former paper … these scales may represent electrified clouds…. The horizontal motion of the scales over the floor may represent the motion of the clouds over the earth, and the erect iron punch a hill or high building; and then we see how electrified clouds, passing over hills or high buildings at too great a height to strike, may be attracted lower till within their striking distance; and lastly, if a needle fixed on the punch, with its point upright, or even on the floor below the punch, will draw the fire from the scale silently at a much greater than the striking distance, and so prevent its descending towards the punch; or if in its course it would have come nigh enough to strike, yet, being first deprived of its fire, it cannot, and the punch is thereby secured from its stroke;—I say, if these things are so, may not the knowledge of this power of points be of use to mankind, in preserving houses, churches, ships, etc., from the stroke of the lightning, by directing us to fix, on the highest parts of those edifices, upright rods of iron made sharp as a needle, and gilt to prevent rusting, and from the foot of those rods a wire down the outside of the building into the ground, or down round one of the shrouds of a ship, and down her side till it reaches the water? Would not these pointed rods probably draw the electrical fire silently out of a cloud before it came nigh enough to strike, and thereby secure us from that most sudden and terrible mischief?"

Franklin goes on to suggest the possibility of obtaining electricity from the clouds by means of a pointed rod fixed on the top of a high building and insulated. Such a rod he afterwards erected in his own house. Another rod connected to the earth he brought within six inches of it, and, attaching a small bell to each rod, he suspended a little ball or clapper by a silk thread, so that it could strike either bell when attracted to it. On the approach of a thunder-cloud, and occasionally when no clouds were near, the bells would ring, indicating that the rod had become strongly electrified. On one occasion Franklin was disturbed by a loud noise, and, coming out of his bedroom, he found an apparently continuous and very luminous discharge taking place between the bells, forming a stream of fire about as large as a pencil.

A very pretty experiment of Franklin's was that of the *golden fish*. A small piece of gold-leaf is cut into a quadrilateral having one of its angles about 150°, the opposite angle about 30°, and the other two right angles. "If you take it by the tail, and hold it at a foot or greater horizontal distance from the prime conductor, it will, when let go, fly to it with a brisk but wavering motion, like that of an eel through the water; it will then take place under the prime conductor, at perhaps a quarter or half an inch distance, and keep a continual shaking of its tail like a fish, so that it seems animated. Turn its tail towards the prime conductor, and then it flies to your finger, and seems to nibble it. And if you hold a [pewter] plate under it at six or eight inches distance, and cease turning the globe, when the electrical atmosphere of the conductor grows small it will descend to the plate and swim back again several times with the same fish-like motion; greatly to the entertainment of spectators. By a little practice in blunting or sharpening the heads or tails of these figures, you may make them take place as desired, nearer or further from the electrified plate."

By the discharge of the battery, Franklin succeeded in melting and volatilizing gold-leaf, thin strips of tinfoil, etc. His views on the nature of light are best given in his own words.

"I am not satisfied with the doctrine that supposes particles of matter called light, continually driven off from the sun's surface, with a swiftness so prodigious! Must not the smallest particle conceivable have, with such a motion, a force exceeding that of a twenty-four pounder discharged from a cannon?... Yet these particles, with this amazing motion, will not drive before them, or remove, the least and lightest dust they meet with.

"May not all the phenomena of light be more conveniently solved by supposing universal space filled with a subtile elastic fluid, which, when at rest, is not visible, but whose vibrations affect that fine sense in the eye, as those of air do the grosser organs of the ear? We do not, in the case of sound, imagine that any sonorous particles are thrown off from a bell, for instance, and fly in straight lines to the ear; why must we believe that luminous particles leave the sun and proceed to the eye? Some diamonds, if rubbed, shine in the dark without losing any part of their matter. I can make an electrical spark as big as the flame of a candle, much brighter, and therefore visible further; yet this is without fuel; and I am persuaded no part of the electrical fluid flies off in such case to distant places, but all goes directly and is to be found in the place to which I destine it. May not different degrees of the vibration of the abovementioned universal medium occasion the appearances of different colours? I think the electric fluid is always the same; yet I find that weaker and stronger sparks differ in apparent colour, some white, blue, purple, red: the strongest, white; weak ones, red. Thus different degrees of vibration given to the air produce the seven different sounds in music, analogous to the seven colours, yet the medium, air, is the same."

Mr. Kinnersley having called Franklin's attention to the fact that a sulphur globe when rubbed produced electrification of an opposite kind from that produced by a glass globe, Franklin repeated the experiment, and noticed that the discharge from the end of a wire connected with the conductor was different in the two cases, being "long, large, and much diverging when the glass globe is used, and makes a snapping (or rattling) noise; but when the sulphur one is used it is short, small, and makes a hissing noise; and just the reverse of both happens when you hold the same wire in your hand and the globes are worked alternately…. When the brush is long, large, and much diverging, the body to which it is joined seems to be throwing the fire out; and when the contrary appears it seems to be drinking in."

On October 19, 1752, Franklin wrote to Mr. Peter Collinson as follows:—

As frequent mention is made in public papers from Europe of the success of the Philadelphia experiment for drawing the electric fire from clouds by means of pointed rods of iron erected on high buildings, etc., it may be agreeable to the curious to be informed that the same experiment has succeeded in Philadelphia, though made in a different and more easy manner, which is as follows:—

Make a small cross of two light strips of cedar, the arms so long as to reach to the four corners of a large thin silk handkerchief when extended. Tie the corners of the handkerchief to the extremities of the cross, so you have the body of a kite; which, being properly accommodated with a tail, loop, and string, will rise in the air like those made of paper; but this being of silk is fitter to bear the wet and wind of a thunder-gust without tearing. To the top of the upright stick of the cross is to be fixed a very sharp-pointed wire, rising a foot or more above the wood. To the end of the twine, next the hand, is to be tied a silk ribbon, and, where the silk and twine join, a key may be fastened. This kite is to be raised when a thunder-gust appears to be coming on, and the person who holds the string must stand within a door or window, or under some cover so that the silk ribbon may not be wet, and care must be taken that the twine does not touch the frame of the door or window. As soon as any of the thunder-clouds come over the kite, the pointed wire will draw the electric fire from them, and the kite, with all the twine, will be electrified, and the loose filaments of the twine will stand out every way, and be attracted by an approaching finger. And when the rain has wetted the kite and twine so that it can conduct the electric fire freely, you will find it stream out plentifully from the key on the approach of your knuckle. At this key the phial may be charged, and from electric fire there obtained spirits may be kindled, and all the other electric experiments be performed which are usually done by the help of a rubbed glass globe or tube, and thereby the sameness of the electric matter with that of lightning completely demonstrated.

Having, in September, 1752, erected the iron rod and bells in his own house, as previously mentioned, Franklin succeeded, in April, 1753, in charging a Leyden jar from the rod, and found its charge was negative. On June 6, however, he obtained a positive charge from a cloud. The results of his observations led him to the conclusion *"That the clouds of a thunder-gust are most commonly in a negative state of electricity, but sometimes in a positive state."*

In order to illustrate a theory respecting the electrification of clouds, Franklin placed a silver can on a wine-glass. Inside the can was placed a considerable length of chain, which could be drawn out by means of a silk thread. He electrified the can from a Leyden jar until it would receive no more electricity. Then raising the silk thread, he gradually drew the chain out of the can, and found that the greater the length of chain drawn out the greater was the charge which the jar would give to the system, and as the chain was raised, spark after spark passed from the jar to the silver can, thus showing that the capacity of the system was increased by increasing the amount of chain exposed.

In 1755 Franklin observed the effects of induction; for, having attached to his prime conductor a tassel made of damp threads and electrified the conductor, he found that the threads repelled each other and stood out. Bringing an excited glass tube near the other end of the conductor, the threads were found to diverge more, "because the atmosphere of the prime conductor is pressed by the atmosphere of the excited tube, and driven towards the end where the threads are, by which each thread acquires more atmosphere." When the excited tube was brought near the threads, they closed a little, "because the atmosphere of the glass tube repels their atmospheres, and drives part of them back on the prime conductor." A number of other experiments illustrating electrical induction were also carried out.

In writing to Dr. Living, of Charlestown, under date March 18, 1755, Franklin gave the following extracts of the minutes of his experiments as explaining the train of thought which led him to attempt to obtain electricity from the clouds:—

"November 7, 1749. Electrical fluid agrees with lightning in these particulars: 1. Giving light. 2. Colour of the light. 3. Crooked direction. 4. Swift motion. 5. Being conducted by metals. 6. Crack or noise in exploding. 7. Subsisting in water or ice. 8. Rending bodies it passes through. 9. Destroying animals. 10. Melting metals. 11. Firing inflammable substances. 12. Sulphureous smell. The electric fluid is attracted by points. We do not know whether this property is in lightning. But since they agree in all the particulars wherein we can already compare them, is it not probable they agree likewise in this? Let the

experiment be made."

Another experiment very important in its bearing on the theory of electricity was described by Franklin in the same letter to Dr. Living. It was afterwards repeated in a much more complete form by Cavendish, who deduced from it the great law that electrical repulsion varies inversely as the square of the distance between the charges. The same experiment was repeated in other forms by Faraday, who had no means of knowing what Cavendish had done. Franklin writes:—

> I electrified a silver fruit-can on an electric stand, and then lowered into it a cork ball of about an inch in diameter, hanging by a silk string, till the cork touched the bottom of the can. The cork was not attracted to the inside of the can, as it would have been to the outside, and though it touched the bottom, yet, when drawn out, it was not found to be electrified by that touch, as it would have been by touching the outside. The fact is singular. You require the reason? I do not know it. Perhaps you may discover it, and then you will be so good as to communicate it to me. I find a frank acknowledgment of one's ignorance is not only the easiest way to get rid of a difficulty, but the likeliest way to obtain information, and therefore I practise it. I think it is an honest policy.

A note appended to this letter runs as follows:—

> Mr. F. has since thought that, possibly, the mutual repulsion of the inner opposite sides of the electrized can may prevent the accumulating an electric atmosphere upon them, and occasion it to stand chiefly on the outside. But recommends it to the further examination of the curious.

The explanation in this note is the correct one, and from the fact that in the case of a completely closed hollow conductor the charge is not only *chiefly* but *wholly* on the outside, the law of inverse squares above referred to follows as a mathematical consequence.

On writing to M. Dalibard, of Paris, on June 29, 1755, Franklin complained that, though he always (except once) assigned to lightning-rods the alternative duty of either *preventing* a stroke or of *conducting* the lightning with safety to the ground, yet in Europe attention was paid only to the *prevention* of the stroke, which was only a *part* of the duty assigned to the conductors. This is followed by the description of the effect of a stroke upon a church-steeple at Newbury, in New England. The spire was split all to pieces, so that nothing remained above the bell. The lightning then passed down a wire to the clock, then down the pendulum, without injury to the building. "From the end of the pendulum, down quite to the ground, the building was exceedingly rent and damaged, and some stones in the foundation-wall torn out and thrown to the distance of twenty or thirty feet." The pendulum-rod was uninjured, but the fine wire leading from the bell to the clock was vaporized except for about two inches at each end.

Mr. James Alexander, of New York, having proposed to Franklin that the velocity of the electric discharge might be measured by discharging a jar through a long circuit of river-water, Franklin, in his reply, explained that such an experiment, if successful, would not determine the actual velocity of electricity in the conductor. He compared the electricity in conductors to an incompressible fluid, so that when a little additional fluid is injected at one end of a conductor, an equal amount must be extruded at the other end—his view apparently being identical with that of Maxwell, who held that all electric displacements must take place *in closed circuits*.

"Suppose a tube of any length open at both ends.... If the tube be filled with water, and I inject an additional inch of water at one end, I force out an equal quantity at the other in the very same instant.

"And the water forced out at one end of the tube is not the very same water that was forced in at the other end at the same time; it was only one motion at the same time.

"The long wire, made use of in the experiment to discover the velocity of the electric fluid, is itself filled with what we call its natural quantity of that fluid, before the hook of the Leyden bottle is applied at one end of it.

"The outside of the bottle being at the time of such application in contact with the other end of the wire, the whole quantity of electric fluid contained in the wire is, probably, put in motion at once.

"For at the instant the hook, connected with the inside of the bottle, *gives out*, the coating or outside of the bottle *draws in*, a portion of that fluid....

"So that this experiment only shows the extreme facility with which the electric fluid moves in metal; it can never determine the velocity.

"And, therefore, the proposed experiment (though well imagined and very ingenious) of sending the spark round through a vast length of space, by the waters of Susquehannah, or Potowmack, and Ohio, would not afford the satisfaction desired, though we could be sure that the motion of the electric fluid would be in that tract, and not underground in the wet earth by the shortest way."

In his investigations of the source of electricity in thunder-clouds, Franklin tried an experiment which has been frequently repeated with various modifications. Having insulated a large brass plate which had been previously heated, he sprinkled water upon it, in order, if possible, to obtain electricity by the evaporation of the water, but no trace of electrification could be detected.

During his visit to England, Franklin wrote many letters to Mr. Kinnersley and others on philosophical questions, but they consisted mainly of accounts of the work done by other experimenters in England, his public business occupying too much of his attention to allow him to conduct investigations for himself. In one of his letters, speaking of Lord Charles Cavendish, he says:—

It were to be wished that this noble philosopher would communicate more of his experiments to the world, as he makes many, and with great accuracy.

When the controversy between the relative merits of points and knobs for the terminals of lightning-conductors arose, Franklin wrote to Mr. Kinnersley:—

Here are some electricians that recommend knobs instead of points on the upper end of the rods, from a supposition that the points invite the stroke. It is true that points draw electricity at greater distances in the gradual silent way; but knobs will draw at the greatest distance a stroke. There is an experiment which will settle this. Take a crooked wire of the thickness of a quill, and of such a length as that, one end of it being applied to the lower part of a charged bottle, the upper may be brought near the ball on the top of the wire that is in the bottle. Let one end of this wire be furnished with a knob, and the other may be gradually tapered to a fine point. When the point is presented to discharge the bottle, it must be brought much nearer before it will receive the stroke than the knob requires to be. Points, besides, tend to repel the fragments of an electrical cloud; knobs draw them nearer. An experiment, which I believe I have shown you, of cotton fleece hanging from an electrized body, shows this clearly when a point or a knob is presented under it.

The following quotation from Franklin's paper on the method of securing buildings and persons from the effects of lightning is worthy of attention, for of late years a good deal of money has been wasted in providing insulators for lightning-rods. A few years ago the vicar and churchwardens of a Lincolnshire parish were strongly urged to go to the expense of insulating the conductor throughout the whole height of the very lofty tower and spire of their parish church. Happily they were wise enough to send the lightning-rod man about his business. But this is not the only case which has come under the writer's notice, showing that there is still a widespread impression that lightning-conductors should be carefully insulated. Franklin says:—

"The rod may be fastened to the wall, chimney, etc., with staples of iron. The lightning will not leave the rod (a good conductor) to pass into the wall (a bad conductor) through these staples. It would rather, if any were in the wall, pass out of it into the rod, to get more readily by that conductor into the earth."[2]

[2] See p. 141.

The conditions to be secured in a lightning-conductor are, firstly, a sharp point projecting above the highest part of the building, and gilded to prevent corrosion; secondly, metallic continuity from the point to the lower end of the conductor; and, thirdly, a good earth-contact. The last can frequently be secured by soldering the conductor to iron water-pipes underground. Where these are not available, a copper plate, two or three feet square, imbedded in clay or other damp earth, will serve the purpose. The method of securing a building which is erected on granite or other foundation affording no good earth-connection, will be referred to in a subsequent biographical sketch.

The controversy of points *versus* knobs was again revived in London when Franklin was in Paris, and the War of Independence had begun. Franklin was consulted on the subject, the question having arisen in connection with the conductor at the palace. His reply was characteristic.

"As to my writing anything on the subject, which you seem to desire, I think it not necessary, especially as I have nothing to add to what I have already said upon it in a paper read to the committee who ordered the conductors at Purfleet, which paper is printed in the last French edition of my writings.

"I have never entered into any controversy in defence of my philosophical opinions. I leave them to take their chance in the world. If they are *right*, truth and experience will support them; if *wrong*, they ought to be refuted and rejected. Disputes are apt to sour one's temper and disturb one's quiet. I have no private interest in the reception of my inventions by the world, having never made, nor proposed to make, the least profit by any of them. The king's changing his *pointed* conductors for *blunt* ones is, therefore, a matter of small importance to me. If I had a wish about it, it would be that he had rejected them altogether as ineffectual. For it is only since he thought himself and family safe from the thunder of Heaven, that he dared to use his own thunder in destroying his innocent subjects."

The paper referred to was read before "the committee appointed to consider the erecting conductors to secure the magazines at Purfleet," on August 27, 1772. It described a variety of experiments clearly demonstrating the effect of points in discharging a conductor. This was a committee of the Royal Society, to whom the question had been referred on account of Dr. Wilson's recommendation of a blunt conductor. The committee decided in favour of Franklin's view, and when, in 1777, the question was again raised and again referred to a committee of the Royal Society, the decision of the former committee was confirmed, "conceiving that the experiments and reasons made and alleged to the contrary by Mr. Wilson are inconclusive."

Though Franklin's scientific reputation rests mainly on his electrical researches, he did not leave other branches of science untouched. Besides his work on atmospheric electricity, he devoted a great deal of thought to meteorology, especially to the vortical motion of waterspouts. The Gulf-stream received a share of his attention. His improvements in fireplaces have already been noticed; the cure of smoky chimneys was the subject of a long paper addressed to Dr. Ingenhousz, and of some other letters. One of his experiments on the absorption of radiant energy has been deservedly remembered.

"My experiment was this: I took a number of little square pieces of broad-cloth from a tailor's pattern-card, of various colours. There were black, deep blue, lighter blue, green, purple, red, yellow, white, and other colours or shades of colours. I laid them all out upon the snow in a bright, sun-shiny morning. In a few hours (I cannot now be exact as to the time) the black, being warmed most by the sun, was sunk so low as to be below the stroke of the sun's rays; the dark blue almost as low, the lighter blue not quite so much as the dark, the other colours less as they were lighter; and the quite white remained on the surface of the snow, not having entered it at all.

"What signifies philosophy that does not apply to some use? May we not learn from hence that black clothes are not so fit to wear in a hot, sunny climate or season, as white ones?"

Franklin knew much about electricity, but his knowledge of human nature was deeper still. This appears in all his transactions. His political economy was, perhaps, not always sound, but his judgment of men was seldom at fault.

"Finally, there seem to be but three ways for a nation to acquire wealth. The first is by *war*, as the Romans did, in plundering their conquered neighbour: this is *robbery*. The second by *commerce*, which is generally *cheating*. The third by *agriculture*, the only *honest way*, wherein man receives a real increase of the seed thrown into the ground, in a kind of continual miracle wrought by the hand of God in his favour, as a reward for his innocent life and his virtuous industry."

When Franklin reached London in 1757 he took up his abode with Mrs. Margaret Stevenson, in Craven Street, Strand. For Mrs. Stevenson and her daughter Mary, then a young lady of eighteen, he acquired a sincere affection, which continued throughout their lives. Miss Stevenson spent much of her time with an aunt in the country, and some of Franklin's letters to her respecting the conduct of her "higher education" are among the most interesting of his writings. Miss Stevenson treated him as a father, and consulted him on every question of importance in her life. When she was a widow and Franklin eighty years of age, he urged upon her to come to

Philadelphia, for the sake of the better prospects which the new country offered her boys. In coming to England, Franklin brought with him his son William, who entered the Middle Temple, but he left behind his only daughter, Sarah, in charge of her mother. To his wife and daughter he frequently sent presents from London, and his letters to Mrs. Franklin give a pretty full account of all his doings while in England. During his visit he received the honorary degrees of D.C.L. from the University of Oxford, and LL.D. from that of Edinburgh. At Cambridge he was sumptuously entertained. In August, 1762, he started again for America, and reached Philadelphia on November 1, after an absence of five years. His son William had shortly before been appointed Governor of New Jersey. From this time William Franklin became very much the servant of the proprietaries and of the English Government, but no offer of patronage produced any effect on the father.

Franklin's stay in America was of short duration, but while there he was mainly instrumental in quelling an insurrection in Pennsylvania. He made a tour of inspection through the northern colonies in the summer of 1763, to regulate the post-offices. The disorder just referred to in the province caused the governor, as well as the Assembly, to determine on the formation of a militia. A committee, of which Franklin was a member, drew up the necessary bill. The governor claimed the sole power of appointing officers, and required that trials should be by court-martial, some offences being punishable with death. The Assembly refused to agree to these considerations. The ill feeling was increased by the governor insisting on taxing all proprietary lands at the same rate as uncultivated land belonging to other persons, whether the proprietary lands were cultivated or not. The Assembly, before adjourning, expressed an opinion that peace and happiness would not be secured until the government was lodged directly in the Crown. When the Assembly again met, petitions to the king came in from more than three thousand inhabitants. In the mean while the British Ministry had proposed the Stamp Act, which was similar in principle to the English Stamp Act, which requires that all agreements, receipts, bills of exchange, marriage and birth certificates, and all other legal documents should be provided with an inland revenue stamp of a particular value, in order that they might be valid. As soon as the Assembly was convened, it determined to send Franklin to England, to take charge of a petition for a change of government. The merchants subscribed £1100 towards his expenses in a few hours, and in twelve days he was on his journey, being accompanied to the ship, a distance of sixteen miles, by a cavalcade of three hundred of his friends, and in thirty days he reached London. Arrived in London, he at once took up his abode in his old lodgings with Mrs. Stevenson. He was a master of satire, equalled only by Swift, and during the quarrels which preceded the War of Independence, as well as during the war, he made good use of his powers in this respect. Articles appeared in some of the English papers tending to raise an alarm respecting the competition of the colonies with English manufacturers. Franklin's contribution to the discussion was a caricature of the English press writers.

"It is objected by superficial readers, who yet pretend to some knowledge of those countries, that such establishments [manufactories for woollen goods, etc.] are not only improbable, but impossible, for that their sheep have but little wool, not in the whole sufficient for a pair of stockings a year to each inhabitant; that, from the universal dearness of labour among them, the working of iron and other materials, except in a few coarse instances, is impracticable to any advantage.

"Dear sir, do not let us suffer ourselves to be amused with such groundless objections. The very tails of the American sheep are so laden with wool that each has a little car or waggon on four little wheels to support and keep it from trailing on the ground. Would they caulk their ships, would they even litter their horses with wool, if it were not both plenty and cheap? And what signifies the dearness of labour, when an English shilling passes for five and twenty? Their engaging three hundred silk throwsters here in one week for New York was treated as a fable, because, forsooth, they have 'no silk there to throw!' Those who make this objection perhaps do not know that, at the same time, the agents for the King of Spain were at Quebec, to contract for one thousand pieces of cannon to be made there for the fortification of Mexico, and at New York engaging the usual supply of woollen floor-carpets for their West India houses. Other agents from the Emperor of China were at Boston, treating about an exchange of raw silk for wool, to be carried in Chinese junks through the Straits of Magellan.

"And yet all this is as certainly true as the account said to be from Quebec in all the papers of last week, that the inhabitants of Canada are making preparations for a cod and whale fishery this summer in the upper Lakes. Ignorant people may object that the upper Lakes are fresh, and that cod and whales are salt-water fish; but let them know, sir, that cod, like other fish when attacked by their enemies, fly into any water where they can be safest; that whales, when they have a mind to eat cod, pursue them wherever they fly; and that the grand leap of the whale in the chase up the Falls of Niagara is esteemed, by all who have seen it, as one of the finest spectacles in nature."

One of Franklin's chief objects in coming to England was to prevent the passing of Mr. Grenville's bill, previously referred to as the Stamp Act. The colonists urged that they had always been liberal in their votes, whenever money was required by the Crown, and that taxation and representation must, in accordance with the British constitution, go hand-in-hand, so that the English Parliament had no right to raise taxes in America, so long as the colonists were unrepresented in Parliament. "Had Mr. Grenville, instead of that act, applied to the king in Council for such requisitional letters [*i.e.* requests to the Assemblies for voluntary grants], to be circulated by the Secretary of State, I am sure he would have obtained more money from the colonies by their voluntary grants than he himself expected from the sale of stamps. But he chose compulsion rather than persuasion, and would not receive from their good will what he thought he could obtain without it." The Stamp Act was passed, stamps were printed, distributors were appointed, but the colonists would have nothing to do with the stamps. The distributors were compelled to resign their commissions, and the captains of vessels were forbidden to land the stamped paper. The cost of printing and distributing amounted to £12,000; the whole return was about £1500, from Canada and the West Indies.

The passing of the Stamp Act was soon followed by a change of Ministry, when the question again came before Parliament. Franklin submitted to a long examination before a Committee of the whole House. The feeling prevalent in America respecting the Stamp Act may be inferred from some of his answers.

"31. *Q.* Do you think the people of America would submit to pay the stamp duty if it was moderated?

"*A.* No, never, unless compelled by force of arms.

"36. *Q.* What was the temper of America towards Great Britain before the year 1763?[3]

> [3] The date of the Sugar Act.

"*A.* The best in the world. They submitted willingly to the government of the Crown, and paid, in their courts, obedience to the Acts of Parliament. Numerous as the people are in the several old provinces, they cost you nothing in forts, citadels, garrisons, or armies to keep them in subjection. They were governed by this country at the expense only of a little pen, ink, and paper; they were led by a thread. They had not only a respect, but an affection, for Great Britain—for its laws, its customs and manners, and even a fondness for its fashions, that greatly increased the commerce. Natives of Britain were always treated with particular regard; to be an *Old-Englandman* was, of itself, a character of some respect, and gave a kind of rank among us.

"37. *Q.* And what is their temper now?

"*A.* Oh, very much altered.

"50. *Q.* Was it an opinion in America before 1763 that the Parliament had no right to lay taxes and duties there?

"*A.* I never heard any objection to the right of laying duties to regulate commerce; but a right to lay internal taxes was never supposed to be in Parliament, as we are not represented there.

"59. *Q.* You say the colonies have always submitted to external taxes, and object to the right of Parliament only in laying internal taxes; now, can you show that there is any kind of difference between the two taxes to the colony on which they may be laid?

"*A.* I think the difference is very great. An *external* tax is a duty laid on commodities imported; that duty is added to the first cost and other charges on the commodity, and, when it is offered to sale, makes a part of the price. If the people do not like it at that price, they refuse it; they are not obliged to pay it. But an *internal* tax is forced upon the people without their consent, if not laid by their own representatives. The Stamp Act says we shall have no commerce, make no exchange of property with each other, neither purchase, nor grant, nor recover debts; we shall neither marry nor make our wills, unless we pay such and such sums; and thus it is intended to extort our money from us, or ruin us by the consequences of refusing to pay it.

"61. *Q.* Don't you think cloth from England absolutely necessary to them?

"*A.* No, by no means absolutely necessary; with industry and good management they may very well supply themselves with all they want.

"62. *Q.* Will it not take a long time to establish that manufacture among them? and must they not in the mean while suffer greatly?

"*A.* I think not. They have made a surprising progress already. And I am of opinion that, before their old clothes are worn out, they will have new ones of their own making.

"84. *Q.* If the Act is not repealed, what do you think will be the consequence?

"*A.* A total loss of the respect and affection the people of America bear to this country, and of all the commerce that depends on that respect and affection.

"85. *Q.* How can the commerce be affected?

"*A.* You will find that, if the Act is not repealed, they will take a very little of your manufactures in a short time.

"86. *Q.* Is it in their power to do without them?

"*A.* I think they may very well do without them.

"87. *Q.* Is it their interest not to take them?

"*A*. The goods they take from Britain are either necessaries, mere conveniences, or superfluities. The first, as cloth, etc., with a little industry they can make at home; the second they can do without till they are able to provide them among themselves; and the last, which are much the greatest part, they will strike off immediately. They are mere articles of fashion, purchased and consumed because the fashion in a respected country; but will now be detested and rejected. The people have already struck off, by general agreement, the use of all goods fashionable in mournings, and many thousand pounds' worth are sent back as unsaleable.

"173. *Q*. What used to be the pride of the Americans?

"*A*. To indulge in the fashions and manufactures of Great Britain.

"174. *Q*. What is now their pride?

"*A*. To wear their old clothes over again till they can make new ones."

The month following Franklin's examination, the repeal of the Stamp Act received the royal assent. Thereupon Franklin sent his wife and daughter new dresses, and a number of other little luxuries (or toilet necessaries).

In 1767 Franklin visited Paris. In the same year his daughter married Mr. Richard Bache. Though Parliament had repealed the Stamp Act, it nevertheless insisted on its right to tax the colonies. The Duty Act was scarcely less objectionable than its predecessor. On Franklin's return from the Continent, he heard of the retaliatory measures of the Boston people, who had assembled in town-meetings, formally resolved to encourage home manufactures, to abandon superfluities, and, after a certain time, to give up the use of some articles of foreign manufacture. These *associations* afterwards became very general in the colonies, so that in one year the importations by the colonists of New York fell from £482,000 to £74,000, and in Pennsylvania from £432,000 to £119,000.

The effect of the Duty Act was to encourage the Dutch and other nations to smuggle tea and probably other India produce into America. The exclusion from the American markets of tea sent from England placed the East India Company in great difficulties; for while they were unable to meet their bills, they had in stock two million pounds' worth of tea and other goods. The balance of the revenue collected under the Duty Act, after paying salaries, etc., amounted to only £85 for the year, and for this a fleet had to be maintained, to guard the fifteen hundred miles of American coast; while the fall in East India Stock deprived the revenue of £400,000 per annum, which the East India Company would otherwise have paid. At length a licence was granted to the East India Company to carry tea into America, duty free. This, of course, excluded all other merchants from the American tea-trade. A quantity of tea sent by the East India Company to Boston was destroyed by the people. The British Government then blockaded the port. This soon led to open hostilities. Franklin worked hard to effect a reconciliation. He drew up a scheme, setting forth the conditions under which he conceived a reconciliation might be brought about, and discussed it fully with Mr. Daniel Barclay and Dr. Fothergill. This scheme was shown to Lord Howe, and afterwards brought before the Ministry, but was rejected. Other plans were considered, and Franklin offered to pay for the tea which had been destroyed at Boston. All his negotiations were, however, fruitless. At last he addressed a memorial to the Earl of Dartmouth, Secretary of State, complaining of the blockade of Boston, which had then continued for nine months, and had "during every week of its continuance done damage to that town, equal to what was suffered there by the India Company;" and claiming reparation for such injury beyond the value of the tea which had been destroyed. The memorial also complained of the exclusion of the colonists from the Newfoundland fisheries, for which reparation would one day be required. This memorial was returned to Franklin by Mr. Walpole, and Franklin shortly afterwards returned to Philadelphia.

During this visit to England he had lost his wife, who died on December 19, 1774; and his friend Miss Stevenson had married and been left a widow.

In April, 1768, Franklin was appointed Agent for Georgia, in the following year for New Jersey, and in 1770 for Massachusetts, so that he was then the representative in England of four colonies, with an income of £1200 per annum.

In 1771 he spent three weeks at Twyford, with the Bishop of St. Asaph, who remained a fast friend of Franklin's until his death. In 1772 he was nominated by the King of France as Foreign Associate of the Academy of Sciences.

During his negotiations with the British Government Franklin wrote two satirical pieces, setting forth the treatment which the American colonists were receiving. The first was entitled "Rules for Reducing a Great Empire to a Small One," the rules being precisely those which, in Franklin's opinion, had been followed by the British Government in its dealings with America. The other was "An Edict by the King of Prussia," in which the king claimed the right of taxing the British nation; of forbidding English manufacture, and compelling Englishmen to purchase Prussian goods; of transporting prisoners to Britain, and generally of exercising all such controls over the English people as had been claimed over America by various Acts of the English Parliament, on the ground that England was originally colonized by emigrants from Prussia.

Before Franklin reached America, the War of Independence, though not formally declared, had fairly begun. He was appointed a member of the second Continental Congress, and one of a committee of three to confer with General Washington respecting the support and regulation of the Continental Army. This latter office necessitated his spending some time in the camp. On October 3, 1775, he wrote to Priestley:—

> Tell our dear good friend, Dr. Price, who sometimes has his doubts and despondencies about our firmness, that America is determined and unanimous; a very few Tories and placemen excepted, who will probably soon export themselves. Britain, at the expense of three millions, has killed a hundred and fifty Yankees this campaign, which is £20,000 a head; and at Bunker's Hill she gained a mile of ground, half of which she lost again by our taking the post on Ploughed Hill. During the same time sixty thousand children have been born in America. From these *data* his mathematical head will easily calculate the time and expense necessary to kill us all and conquer our whole territory.

In 1776 Franklin, then seventy years old, was appointed one of three Commissioners to visit Canada, in order, if possible, to promote a union between it and the States. Finding that only one Canadian in five hundred could read, and that the state of feeling in Canada was fatal to the success of the Commissioners, they returned, and Franklin suggested that the next Commission sent to Canada should consist of schoolmasters. On the 4th of July Franklin took part in the signing of the Declaration of Independence. When the document was about to be signed, Mr. Hancock remarked, "We must be unanimous; there must be no pulling different ways; we must all hang together." Franklin replied, "Yes, we must indeed all hang together, or most assuredly we shall all hang separately."

In the autumn of 1776 Franklin was unanimously chosen a Special Commissioner to the French Court. He took with him his two grandsons, William Temple Franklin and Benjamin Franklin Bache, and leaving Marcus Hook on October 28, crossed the Atlantic in a sloop of sixteen guns. In Paris he met with an enthusiastic reception. M. de Chaumont placed at his disposal his house at Passy, then about a mile from Paris, but now within the city. Here he resided for nine years, being a constant visitor at the French Court, and certainly one of the most conspicuous figures in Paris. He was obliged to serve in many capacities, and was very much burdened with work. Not only were there his duties as Commissioner at the French Court, but he was also made Admiralty Judge and Financial Agent, so that all the coupons for the payment of interest on the money borrowed for the prosecution of the war, as well as all financial negotiations, either with the French Government or contractors, had to pass through his hands. Perhaps the most unpleasant part of his work was his continued applications to the French Court for monetary advances. The French Government, as is well known, warmly espoused the cause of the Americans, and to the utmost of its ability assisted them with money, material, and men. Franklin was worried a good deal by applications from French officers for introductions to General Washington, that they might obtain employment in the American Army. At last he framed a model letter of recommendation, which may be useful to many in this country in the present day. It was as follows:—

"SIR,

The bearer of this, who is going to America, presses me to give him a letter of recommendation, though I know nothing of him, not even his name. This may seem extraordinary, but I assure you it is not uncommon here. Sometimes, indeed, one unknown person brings another equally unknown, to recommend him; and sometimes they recommend one another! As to this gentleman, I must refer you to himself for his character and merits, with which he is certainly better acquainted than I can possibly be. I recommend him, however, to those civilities which every stranger, of whom one knows no harm, has a right to; and I request you will do him all the good offices and show him all the favour that, on further acquaintance, you shall find him to deserve.

I have the honour to be, etc.

Captain Wickes, of the *Refusal*, having taken about a hundred British seamen prisoners, Franklin and Silas Deane, one of the other Commissioners, wrote to Lord Stormont, the British ambassador, respecting an exchange. Receiving no answer, they wrote again, and ventured to complain of the treatment which the American prisoners were receiving in the English prisons, and in being compelled to fight against their own countrymen. To this communication Lord Stormont replied:—

The king's ambassador receives no applications from rebels, unless they come to implore his Majesty's mercy.

To this the Commissioners rejoined:—

In answer to a letter, which concerns some of the most material interests of humanity, and of the two nations, Great Britain and the United States of America, now at war, we received the enclosed *indecent* paper, as coming from your Lordship, which we return for your Lordship's more mature consideration.

At first the British Government, regarding the Americans as rebels, did not treat their prisoners as prisoners of war, but threatened to try them for high treason. Their sufferings in the English prisons were very great. Mr. David Hartley did much to relieve them, and Franklin transmitted money for the purpose. When a treaty had been formed between France and the States, and France had engaged in the war, and when fortune began to turn in favour of the united armies, the American prisoners received better treatment from the English Government, and exchanges took place freely. In April, 1778, Mr. Hartley visited Franklin at Passy, apparently for the purpose of preventing, if possible, the offensive and defensive alliance between America and France. Very many attempts were made to produce a rupture between the French Government and the American Commissioners, but Franklin insisted that no treaty of peace could be made between England and America in which France was not included. In 1779 the other Commissioners were recalled, and Franklin was made Minister Plenipotentiary to the Court of France.

In a letter to Mr. David Hartley, dated February 2, 1780, Franklin showed something of the feelings of the Americans with respect to the English at that time:—

You may have heard that accounts upon oath have been taken in America, by order of Congress, of the British barbarities committed there. It is expected of me to make a school-book of them, and to have thirty-five prints designed here by good artists, and engraved, each expressing one or more of the horrid facts, in order to impress the minds of children and posterity with a deep sense of your bloody and insatiable malice and wickedness. Every kindness I hear of done by an Englishman to an American prisoner makes me resolve not to proceed in the work.

While at Passy, Franklin addressed to the *Journal of Paris* a paper on an economical project for diminishing the cost of light. The proposal was to utilize the sunlight instead of candles, and thereby save to the city of Paris the sum of 96,075,000 livres per annum. His reputation in Paris is shown by the following quotation from a contemporary writer:—

I do not often speak of Mr. Franklin, because the gazettes tell you enough of him. However, I will say to you that our Parisians are no more sensible in their attentions to him than they were towards Voltaire, of whom they have not spoken since the day following his death. Mr. Franklin is besieged, followed, admired, adored, wherever he shows himself, with a fury, a fanaticism, capable no doubt of flattering him and of doing him honour, but which at the same time proves that we shall never be reasonable, and that the virtues and better qualities of our nation will always be balanced by a levity, an inconsequence, and an enthusiasm too excessive to be durable.

Franklin always advocated free trade, even in time of war. He was of opinion that the merchant, the agriculturist, and the fisherman were benefactors to mankind. He condemned privateering in every form, and endeavoured to bring about an agreement between all the civilized powers against the fitting out of privateers. He held that no merchantmen should be interfered with unless carrying war material. He greatly lamented the horrors of the war, but preferred anything to a dishonourable peace. To Priestley he wrote:—

Perhaps as you grow older you may ... repent of having murdered in mephitic air so many honest, harmless mice, and wish that, to prevent mischief, you had used boys and girls instead of them. In what light we are viewed by superior beings may be gathered from a piece of late West India news, which possibly has not yet reached you. A young angel of distinction, being sent down to this world on some business for the first time, had an old courier-spirit assigned him as a guide. They arrived over the seas of Martinico, in the middle of the long day of obstinate fight between the fleets of Rodney and De Grasse. When, through the clouds of smoke, he saw the fire of the guns, the decks covered with mangled limbs and bodies dead or dying; the ships sinking, burning, or blown into the air; and the quantity of pain, misery, and destruction the crews yet alive were thus with so much eagerness dealing round to one another,— he turned angrily to his guide, and said, 'You blundering blockhead, you are ignorant of your business; you undertook to conduct me to the earth, and you have brought me into hell!' 'No, sir,' says the guide, 'I have made no mistake; this is really the earth, and these are men. Devils never treat one another in this cruel manner; they have more sense and more of what men (vainly) call humanity.'

Franklin maintained that it would be far cheaper for a nation to extend its possessions by purchase from other nations than to pay the cost of war for the sake of conquest.

Two British armies, under General Burgoyne and Lord Cornwallis, having been wholly taken prisoners during the war, at last, after two years' negotiations, a definitive treaty of peace was signed on September 3, 1782, between Great Britain and the United States, Franklin being one of the Commissioners for the latter, and Mr. Hartley for the former. On the same day a treaty of peace between Great Britain and France was signed at Versailles. The United States Treaty was ratified by the king on April 9, and therewith terminated the seven years' War of Independence. Franklin celebrated the surrender of the armies of Burgoyne and Cornwallis by a medal, on which the infant Hercules appears strangling two serpents.

When peace was at length realized, a scheme was proposed for an hereditary knighthood of the order of Cincinnatus, to be bestowed upon the American officers who had distinguished themselves in the war. Franklin condemned the hereditary principle. He pointed out that, in the ninth generation, the "young noble" would be only "one five hundred and twelfth part of the present knight," 1022 men and women being counted among his ancestors, reckoning only from the foundation of the knighthood. "Posterity will have much reason to boast of the noble blood of the then existing set of Chevaliers of Cincinnatus."

On May 2, 1785, Franklin received from Congress permission to return to America. He was then in his eightieth year. On July 12 he left Passy for Havre, whence he crossed to Southampton, and there saw for the last time his old friend, the Bishop of St. Asaph, and his family. He reached his home in Philadelphia early in September, and the day after his arrival he received a congratulatory address from the Assembly of Pennsylvania. In the following month he was elected President of the State, and was twice re-elected to the same office, it being contrary to the constitution for any president to be elected for more than three years in succession.

The following extract from a letter, written most probably to Tom Paine, is worthy of the attention of some writers:—

I have read your manuscript with some attention. By the argument it contains against a particular Providence, though you allow a general Providence, you strike at the foundations of all religion. For without the belief of a Providence that takes cognizance of, guards, and guides, and may favour particular persons, there is no motive to worship a Deity, to fear His displeasure, or to pray for His protection. I will not enter into any discussion of your principles, though you seem to desire it. At present I shall only give you my opinion, that, though your reasonings are subtle, and may prevail with some readers, you will not succeed so as to change the general sentiments of mankind on that subject, and the consequence of printing this piece will be a great deal of odium drawn upon yourself, mischief to you, and no benefit to others. He that spits against the wind spits in his own face.

But were you to succeed, do you imagine any good would be done by it? You yourself may find it easy to live a virtuous life without the assistance afforded by religion; you having a clear perception of the advantages of virtue and the disadvantages of vice, and possessing strength of resolution sufficient to enable you to resist common temptations. But think how great a portion of mankind consists of weak and ignorant men and women, and of inexperienced, inconsiderate youth of both sexes, who have need of the motives of religion to restrain them from vice, to support their virtue, and retain them in the practice of it till it becomes *habitual*, which is the great point for its security. And perhaps you are indebted to her originally, that is, to your religious education, for the habits of virtue upon which you now justly value yourself. You might easily display your excellent talents of reasoning upon a less hazardous subject, and thereby obtain a rank with our most distinguished authors. For among us it is not necessary, as among the Hottentots, that a youth, to be raised into the company of men, should prove his manhood by beating his mother.

I would advise you, therefore, not to attempt unchaining the tiger, but to burn this piece before it is seen by any other person; whereby you will save yourself a great deal of mortification by the enemies it may raise against you, and perhaps a good deal of regret and repentance. If men are so wicked *with religion*, what would they be *if without* it? I intend this letter itself as a *proof* of my friendship, and therefore add no *professions* to it; but subscribe simply yours.

During the last few years of his life Franklin suffered from a painful disease, which confined him to his bed and seriously interfered with his literary work, preventing him from completing his biography. During this time he was cared for by his daughter, Mrs. Bache, who resided in the same house with him. He died on April 17, 1790, the immediate cause of death being an affection of the lungs. He was buried beside his wife in the cemetery of Christ Church, Philadelphia, the marble slab upon the grave bearing no other inscription than the name and date of death. In his early days (1728) he had written the following epitaph for himself:—

THE BODY

OF

BENJAMIN FRANKLIN,

PRINTER,

(LIKE THE COVER OF AN OLD BOOK,

ITS CONTENTS TORN OUT

AND STRIPT OF ITS LETTERING AND GILDING,)

LIES HERE, FOOD FOR WORMS.

BUT THE WORK SHALL NOT BE LOST,

THE AUTHOR.

When the news of his death reached the National Assembly of France, Mirabeau rose and said:—

"Franklin is dead!

"The genius, which gave freedom to America, and scattered torrents of light upon Europe, is returned to the bosom of the Divinity.

"The sage, whom two worlds claim; the man, disputed by the history of the sciences and the history of empires, holds, most undoubtedly, an elevated rank among the human species.

"Political cabinets have but too long notified the death of those who were never great but in their funeral orations; the etiquette of courts has but too long sanctioned hypocritical grief. Nations ought only to mourn for their benefactors; the representatives of free men ought never to recommend any other than the heroes of humanity to their homage.

"The Congress hath ordered a general mourning for one month throughout the fourteen confederated States on account of the death of Franklin; and America hath thus acquitted her tribute of admiration in behalf of one of the fathers of her constitution.

"Would it not be worthy of you, fellow-legislators, to unite yourselves in this religious act, to participate in this homage rendered in the face of the universe to the rights of man, and to the philosopher who has so eminently propagated the conquest of them throughout the world?

"Antiquity would have elevated altars to that mortal who, for the advantage of the human race, embracing both heaven and earth in his vast and extensive mind, knew how to subdue thunder and tyranny.

"Enlightened and free, Europe at least owes its remembrance and its regret to one of the greatest men who has ever served the cause of philosophy and liberty.

"I propose, therefore, that a decree do now pass, enacting that the National Assembly shall wear mourning during three days for Benjamin Franklin."

HENRY CAVENDISH.

It would not be easy to mention two men between whom there was a greater contrast, both in respect of their characters and lives, than that which existed between Benjamin Franklin and the Honourable Henry Cavendish. The former of humble birth, but of great public spirit, possessed social qualities which were on a par with his scientific attainments, and toward the close of his life was more renowned as a statesman than as a philosopher; the latter, a member of one of the most noble families of England, and possessed of wealth far exceeding his own capacity for the enjoyment of it, was known to very few, was intimate with no one, and devoted himself to scientific pursuits rather for the sake of the satisfaction which his results afforded to himself than from any hope that they might be useful to mankind, or from any desire to secure a reputation by making them known, and passed a long life, the most uneventful that can be imagined.

Though the records of his family may be traced to the Norman Conquest, the famous Elizabeth Hardwicke, the foundress of two ducal families and the builder of Hardwicke Hall and of Chatsworth as it was before the erection of the present mansion, was the most remarkable person in the genealogy. Her second son, William, was raised to the peerage by James I., thus becoming Baron Cavendish, and was subsequently created first Earl of Devonshire by the same monarch. His great-grandson, the fourth earl, was created first Duke of Devonshire by William III., to whom he had rendered valuable services. He was succeeded by his eldest son in 1707, and the third son of the second duke was Lord Charles Cavendish, the father of Henry and Frederick, of whom Henry was the elder, having been born at Nice, October 13, 1731. His mother died when he was two years old, and very little indeed is known respecting his early life. In 1742 he entered Dr. Newcome's school at Hackney, where he remained until he entered Peterhouse, in 1749. He remained at Cambridge until February, 1753, when he left the university without taking his degree, objecting, most probably, to the religious tests which were then required of all graduates. In this respect his brother Frederick followed his example. On leaving Cambridge Cavendish appears to have resided with his father in Marlborough Street, and to have occasionally assisted him in his scientific experiments, but the investigations of the son soon eclipsed those of the father. It is said that the rooms allotted to Henry Cavendish "were a set of stables, fitted up for his accommodation," and here he carried out many of his experiments, including all those electrical investigations in which he forestalled so much of the work of the present century.

During his father's life, or, at any rate, till within a few years of its close, Henry Cavendish appears to have enjoyed a very narrow income. He frequently dined at the Royal Society Club, and on these occasions would come provided with the five shillings to be paid for the dinner, but no more. Upon his father's death, which took place in 1783, when Henry was more than fifty years of age, his circumstances were very much changed, but it seems that the greater part of his wealth was left him by an uncle who had been an Indian officer, and this legacy may have come into his possession before his father's death. He appears to have been very liberal when it was suggested to him that his assistance would be of service, but it never occurred to him to offer a contribution towards any scientific or public undertaking, and though at the time of his death he is said to have had more money in the funds than any other person in the country, besides a balance of £50,000 on his current account at his bank, and various other property, he bequeathed none to scientific societies or similar institutions. Throughout the latter part of his life he seems to have been quite careless about money, and to have been satisfied if he could only avoid the trouble of attending to his own financial affairs. Hence he would allow enormous sums to accumulate at his banker's, and on one occasion, being present at a christening, and hearing that it was customary for guests to give something to the nurse, he drew from his pocket a handful of guineas, and handed them to her without counting them. After his father's death, Cavendish resided in his own house on Clapham Common. Here a few rooms at the top of the house were made habitable; the rest were filled with apparatus of all descriptions, among which the most numerous examples were thermometers of every kind. He seldom entertained visitors, but when, on rare occasions, a guest had to be entertained, the repast invariably consisted of a leg of mutton. His extreme shyness caused him to dislike all kinds of company, and he had a special aversion to being addressed by a stranger. On one occasion, at a reception given by Sir Joseph Banks, Dr. Ingenhousz introduced to him a distinguished Austrian philosopher, who professed that his main object in coming to England was to obtain a sight of so distinguished a man. Cavendish listened with his gaze fixed on the floor; then, observing a gap in the crowd, he made a rush to the door, nor did he pause till he had reached his carriage. His aversion to women was still greater; his orders for the day he would write out and leave at a stated time on the hall-table, where his house-keeper, at another stated time, would find them. Servants were allowed access to the portion of the house which he occupied only at fixed times when he was away; and having once met a servant on the stairs, a back staircase was immediately erected. His regular walk was down Nightingale Lane to Wandsworth Common, and home by another route. On one occasion, as he was crossing a stile, he saw that he was watched, and thenceforth he took his walks in the evening, but never along the same road. There were only two occasions on which it is recorded that scientific men were admitted to Cavendish's laboratory. The first was in 1775, when Hunter, Priestley, Romayne, Lane, and Nairne were invited to see the experiments with the artificial torpedo. The second was when his experiment on the formation of nitric acid by electric sparks in air had been unsuccessfully attempted by Van Marum, Lavoisier, and Monge, and he "thought it right to take some measures to authenticate the truth of it."

Besides his house at Clapham, Cavendish occupied (by his instruments) a house in Bloomsbury, near the British Museum, while a "mansion" in Dean Street, Soho, was set apart as a library. To this library a number of persons were admitted, who could take out the books on depositing a receipt for them. Cavendish was perfectly methodical in all his actions, and whenever he borrowed one of his own books he duly left the receipt in its place. The only relief to his solitary life was afforded by the meetings of the Royal Society, of which he was elected a Fellow in 1760; by the occasional receptions at the residence of Sir Joseph Banks, P.R.S.; and by his not infrequent dinners with the Royal Society Club at the Crown and Anchor; and he may sometimes have joined the social gatherings of another club which met at the Cat and Bagpipes, in Downing Street. It was to his visits to the Royal Society Club that we are indebted for the only portrait that exists of him. Alexander, the draughtsman to the China Embassy, was bent upon procuring a portrait of Cavendish, and induced a friend to invite him to the club dinner, "where he could easily succeed, by taking his seat near the end of the table, from whence he could sketch the peculiar great-coat of a greyish-green colour, and the remarkable three-cornered hat, invariably worn by Cavendish, and obtain, unobserved, such an outline of the face as, when inserted between the hat and coat, would make, he was quite sure, a full-length portrait that no one could mistake. It was so contrived, and every one who saw it recognized it at once." Another incident is recorded of the Royal Society Club which, perhaps, reflects as much credit upon Cavendish as upon the Society. "One evening we observed a very pretty girl looking out from an upper window on the opposite side of the street, watching the philosophers at dinner. She attracted notice, and one by one we got up and mustered round the window to admire the fair one. Cavendish, who thought we were looking at the moon, hustled up to us in his odd way, and when he saw the real object of our study, turned away with intense disgust, and grunted out, 'Pshaw!'"

In the spring and autumn of 1785, 1786, 1787, and 1793, Cavendish made tours through most of the southern, midland, and western counties, and reached as far north as Whitby. The most memorable of these journeys was that undertaken in 1785, since during its course he visited James Watt at the Soho Works, and manifested great interest in Watt's inventions. This was only two years after the great controversy as to the discovery of the composition of water, but the meeting of the philosophers was of the most friendly character. On all these journeys considerable attention was paid to the geology of the country.

Allusion has already been made to the two committees of the Royal Society to which the questions of the lightning-conductors at Purfleet, and of points *versus* knobs for the terminals of conductors, were referred. Cavendish served on each of these committees, and supported Franklin's view against the recommendation of Mr. Wilson. On the first committee he probably came into personal communication with Franklin himself.

Cavendish's life consisted almost entirely of his philosophical experiments. In other respects it was nearly without incident. He appears to have been so constituted that he must subject everything to accurate measurement. He rarely made experiments which were not *quantitative*; and he may be regarded as the founder of "quantitative philosophy." The labour which he expended over some of his measurements must have been very great, and the accuracy of many of his results is marvellous considering the appliances he had at disposal. When he had satisfied himself with the result of an experiment, he wrote out a full account and preserved it, but very seldom gave it to the public, and when he did publish accounts of any of his investigations it was usually a long time after the experiments had been completed. One of the consequences of his reluctance to publish anything was the long controversy on the discovery of the composition of water, which was revived many years afterwards by Arago's *éloge* on James Watt; but a much more serious result was the loss to the world for so many years of discoveries and measurements which had to be made over again by Faraday, Kohlrausch, and others. The papers he published appeared in the *Philosophical Transactions of the Royal Society*, to which he began to communicate them in 1766. On March 25, 1803, he was elected one of the eight Foreign Associates of the Institute of France. His *éloge* was pronounced by Cuvier, in 1812, who said, "His demeanour and the modest tone of his writings procured him the uncommon distinction of never having his repose disturbed either by jealousy or by criticism." Dr. Wilson says, "He was almost passionless. All that needed for its apprehension more than the pure intellect, or required the exercise of fancy, imagination, affection, or faith, was distasteful to Cavendish. An intellectual head thinking, a pair of wonderfully acute eyes observing, and a pair of very skilful hands experimenting or recording, are all that I realize in reading his memorials." He appeared to have no eye for beauty; he cared nothing for natural scenery, and his apparatus, provided it were efficient, might be clumsy in appearance and of the cheapest materials; but he was extremely particular about accuracy of construction in all essential details. He reminds us of one of our foremost men of science, who, when his attention was directed to the beautiful lantern tower of a cathedral, behind which the full moon was shining, remarked, "I see form and colour, but I don't know what you mean by beauty."

The accounts of Cavendish's death differ to some extent in their details, but otherwise are very similar. It appears that he requested his servant, "as he had something particular to engage his thoughts, and did not wish to be disturbed by any one," to leave him and not to return until a certain hour. When the servant came back, at the time appointed, he found his master dead. This was on February 24, 1810, after an illness of only two or three days.

It is mainly on account of his researches in electricity that the biography of Cavendish finds a place in this volume. These investigations took place between the years 1760 and 1783, and, as already stated, were all conducted in the stables attached to his father's house in Marlborough Street. It was by these experiments that electricity was first brought within the domain of measurement, and many of the numerical results obtained far exceeded in accuracy those of any other observer until the instruments of Sir W. Thomson rendered many electrical measurements a comparatively easy matter. The near agreement of Cavendish's results with those of the best modern electricians has made them a perpetual monument to the genius of their author. It was at the request of Sir W. Thomson, Mr. Charles Tomlinson, and others, that Cavendish's electrical researches might be given to the public, that the Duke of Devonshire, in 1874, entrusted the manuscripts to the care of the late Professor Clerk Maxwell. They had previously been in the hands of Sir William Snow Harris, who reported upon them, but after his death, in 1867, the report could not be found. The papers, with an introduction and a number of very valuable notes by the editor, were published by the Cambridge University Press, just before the death of Clerk Maxwell, in 1879. Sir W. Thomson quotes the following illustration of the accuracy of Cavendish's work:—"I find already that the capacity of a disc was determined experimentally by Cavendish as $1/1 \cdot 57$ of that of a sphere of the same radius. Now we have capacity of disc $= (2/\pi)a = a/1 \cdot 571$!"

Cavendish adopted Franklin's theory of electricity, treating it as an incompressible fluid pervading all bodies, and admitting of displacement only in a closed circuit, unless, indeed, the disturbance might extend to infinity. This fluid he supposed, with Franklin, to be self-repulsive, but to attract matter, while matter devoid of electricity, and therefore in the highest possible condition of negative electrification, he supposed, with Æpinus, to be, like electricity, self-repulsive. One of Cavendish's earliest experiments was the determination of the precise law according to which electrical action varies with the distance between the charges. Franklin had shown that there was no sensible amount of electricity on the interior of a deep hollow vessel, however its exterior surface might be charged. Cavendish mounted a sphere of 12·1 inches in diameter, so that it could be completely enclosed (except where its insulating support passed through) within two hemispheres of 13·3 inches diameter, which were carried by hinged frames, and could thus be allowed to close completely over the sphere, or opened and removed altogether from its neighbourhood. A piece of wire passed through one of the hemispheres so as to touch the inner sphere, but could be removed at pleasure by means of a silk string. The hemispheres being closed with the globe within them, and the wire inserted so as to make communication between the inner and outer spheres, the whole apparatus was electrified by a wire from a charged Leyden jar. This wire was then removed by means of a silken string and "the same motion of the hand which drew away the wire by which the hemispheres were electrified, immediately after that was done, drew out the wire which made the communication between the hemispheres and the inner globe, and, immediately after that was drawn out, separated the hemispheres from each other," and applied the electrometer to the inner globe. "It was also contrived so that the electricity of the hemispheres and of the wire by which they were electrified was discharged as soon as they were separated from each other.... The inner globe and hemispheres were also both coated with tinfoil to make them the more perfect conductors of electricity." The electrometer consisted of a pair of pith-balls; but, though the experiment was several times repeated, they shewed no signs of electrification. From this it was clear that, as there could have been no communication between the globe and hemispheres when the connecting wire was withdrawn, there must have been no electrification on the globe while the hemispheres, though themselves highly charged, surrounded it. To test the delicacy of the experiment, a charge was given to the globe less than one-sixtieth of that previously given to the hemispheres, and this was readily detected by the electrometer. From the result Cavendish inferred that there is no reason to think the inner globe to be at all charged during the experiment. "Hence it follows that the electric attraction and repulsion must be inversely as the square of the distance, and that, when a globe is positively electrified, the redundant fluid in it is lodged entirely on its surface." This conclusion Cavendish showed to be a mathematical consequence of the absence of electrification from the inner sphere; for, were the law otherwise, the inner sphere must be electrified positively or negatively, according as the inverse power were higher or lower than the second, and that the accuracy of the experiment showed the law must lie between the 2 1/50 and the 1 49/50 power of the distance. With his torsion-balance, Coulomb obtained the same law, but Cavendish's method is much easier to carry out, and admits of much greater accuracy than that of

Coulomb. Cavendish's experiment was repeated by Dr. MacAlister, under the superintendence of Clerk Maxwell, in the Cavendish Laboratory, the absence of electrification being tested by Thomson's quadrant electrometer, and it was shown that the deviation from the law of inverse squares could not exceed one in 72,000.

The distinction between *electrical charge* or *quantity of electricity* and "*degree of electrification*" was first clearly made by Cavendish. The latter phrase was subsequently replaced by *intensity*, but *electric intensity* is now used in another sense. Cavendish's phrase, *degree of electrification*, corresponds precisely with our notion of electric *potential*, and is measured by the work done on a unit of electricity by the electric forces in removing it from the point in question to the earth or to infinity. Along with this notion Cavendish introduced the further conception of the amount of electricity required to raise a conductor to a given degree of electrification, that is, the capacity of the conductor. In modern language, the *capacity* of a conductor is defined as "the number of units of electricity required to raise it to unit potential;" and this definition is in precise accordance with the notion of Cavendish, who may be regarded as the founder of the mathematical theory of electricity. Finding that the capacities of similar conductors are proportional to their linear dimensions, he adopted a sphere of one inch diameter as the unit of capacity, and when he speaks of a capacity of so many "inches of electricity," he means a capacity so many times that of his one-inch sphere, or equal to that of a sphere whose diameter is so many inches. The modern unit of capacity in the electro-static system is that of a sphere of *one centimetre radius*, and the capacity of any sphere is numerically equal to its radius expressed in centimetres. Cavendish determined the capacities of nearly all the pieces of apparatus he employed. For this purpose he prepared plates of glass, coated on each side with circles of tinfoil, and arranged in three sets of three, each plate of a set having the same capacity, but each set having three times the capacity of the preceding. There was also a tenth plate, having a capacity equal to the whole of the largest set. The capacity of the ten plates was thus sixty-six times that of one of the smallest set. With these as standards of comparison, he measured the capacities of his other apparatus, and, when possible, modified his conductors so as to make them equal to one of his standards. His large Leyden battery he found to have a capacity of about 321,000 "inches of electricity," so that it was equivalent to a sphere more than five miles in diameter. One of his instruments employed in the measurement of capacities was a "trial plate," consisting of a sheet of metal, with a second sheet which could be made to slide upon it and to lie entirely on the top of the larger plate, or to rest with any portion of its area extending over the edge of the former. This was a conductor whose capacity could be varied at will within certain limits. Finding the capacity of two plates of tinfoil on glass much greater than his calculations led him to expect, Cavendish compared them with two equal plates having air between, and found their capacity very much to exceed that of the air condenser. The same was the case, though in a less degree, with condensers having shellac or bee's-wax for their dielectrics, and thus Cavendish not only discovered the property to which Faraday afterwards gave the name of "specific inductive capacity," but determined its measure in these dielectrics. He also discovered that the apparent capacity of a Leyden jar increases at first for some time after it has been charged—a phenomenon connected with the so-called residual charge of the Leyden jar. Another feature on which he laid some stress, and which was brought to his notice by the comparison of his coated panes, was the creeping of electricity over the surface of the glass beyond the edge of the tinfoil, which had the same effect on the capacity as an increase in the dimensions of the tinfoil. The electricity appeared to spread to a distance of $0 \cdot 07$ inch all round the tinfoil on glass plates whose thickness was $0 \cdot 21$ inch, and $0 \cdot 09$ inch in the case of plates $0 \cdot 08$ inch thick.

His paper on the torpedo was read before the Royal Society in 1776. The experiments were undertaken in order to determine whether the phenomena observed by Mr. John Walsh in connection with the torpedo could be so far imitated by electricity as to justify the conclusion that the shock of the torpedo is an electric discharge. For this purpose Cavendish constructed a wooden torpedo with electrical organs, consisting of a pewter plate on each side, covered with leather. The plates were connected with a charged Leyden battery, by means of wires carried in glass tubes, and thus the battery was discharged through the water in which the torpedo was immersed, and which was rendered of about the same degree of saltness as the sea. Cavendish compared the shock given through the water with that given by the model fish in air, and found the difference much greater than in the case of the real torpedo, but, by increasing the capacity of the battery and diminishing the potential to which it was charged, this discrepancy was diminished, and it was found to be very much less in the case of a second model having a leather, instead of a wooden, body, so that the body of the fish itself offered less resistance to the discharge. One of the chief difficulties lay in the fact that no one had succeeded in obtaining a visible spark from the discharge of the torpedo, which will not pass through the smallest thickness of air. Cavendish accounted for this by supposing the quantity of electricity discharged to be very great, and its potential very small, and showed that the more the charge was increased and the potential diminished in his model, the more closely did it imitate the behaviour of the torpedo.

But the main interest in this paper lies in the indications which it gives that

Cavendish was aware of the laws which regulate the flow of electricity through multiple conductors, and in the comparisons of electrical resistance which are introduced. It had been formerly believed that electricity would always select the shortest or best path, and that the whole of the discharge would take place along that route. Franklin seems to have assumed this in the passage quoted[4] respecting the discharge of the lightning down the uninsulated conductor instead of through the building. The truth, however, is that, when a number of paths are open to an electric current, it will divide itself between them in the inverse ratios of their resistances, or directly as their conductivities, so that, however great the resistance of one of the conductors, some portion, though it may be a very small fraction, of the discharge will take place through it. But this law does not hold in the case of insulators like the air, through which electricity passes only by disruptive discharges, and which completely prevent its passage unless the electro-motive force is sufficient to break through their substance. In the case of the lightning-conductor, however, its resistance is generally so small in comparison with that of the building it is used to protect, that Franklin's conclusion is practically correct.

In his paper on the torpedo Cavendish stated that some experiments had shown that iron wire conducted 400,000,000 times better than rain or distilled water, sea-water 100 times, and saturated solution of sea-salt about 720 times, better than rain-water. Maxwell pointed out that this comparison of iron wire with sea-water would agree almost precisely with the measurements of Matthiesen and Kohlrausch at 11°C. The records of the experiments which led to these results were found among Cavendish's unpublished papers, and the experiments also showed that the conductivity of saline solutions was very nearly proportional to the percentage of salt contained, when this was not very large—a result also obtained long afterwards by Kohlrausch. In making these measurements Cavendish was his own galvanometer. The solutions were contained in glass tubes more than three feet long, and a wire inserted to different distances into the solution; thus the discharge could be made to pass through any length of the liquid column less than that of the tube itself. From the Leyden battery of forty-nine jars, six jars of nearly equal capacity were selected and charged together, and the charge of one jar only was employed for each shock. The discharge passed through the column of liquid contained in the tube, from a wire inserted at the further end, until it reached the sliding wire, when nearly the whole current betook itself to the wire on account of its smaller resistance, and thence passed through the galvanometer, which was Cavendish himself. Two tubes were generally compared together, and the jars discharged alternately through the tubes, and the tube which gave the greatest shock was assumed to possess the least resistance. The wires were then adjusted till the shocks were nearly equal, and positions determined which made the first tube possess a greater and then a less resistance than the second. From these positions the length of the column of liquid was estimated which would make the resistances of the two tubes exactly equal. But the result which has the greatest theoretical interest was obtained by discharging the Leyden jars through wide and narrow tubes containing the same solutions. By these experiments Cavendish found that the resistances of the conductors were independent of the strengths of the currents flowing in them; that is to say, he established Ohm's law for electrolytes in a form which carried with it its full explanation. This was in January, 1781. Ohm's law was first formally stated in 1827. The physical fact which is expressed by it is that the ratio of the electro-motive force to the current produced is the same for the same conductor, otherwise under the same physical conditions, however great or small that electro-motive force may be.

Cavendish devoted considerable attention to the subject of heat, especially thermometry. In many of his investigations on latent and specific heat he worked on the same lines as Black, and at about the same time; but it is difficult to determine the exact date of some of Cavendish's work, as he frequently did not publish it for a long time after its completion, and most of Black's results were made public only to his lecture audience. Cavendish, however, improved upon Black in his mode of stating some of his results. The heat, for instance, which is absorbed by a body in passing from the solid to the liquid, or from the liquid to the gaseous, condition, Black called "latent heat," and supposed it to become latent within the substance, ready to reveal itself when the body returned to its original condition. This heat Cavendish spoke of as being *destroyed* or *generated*, and this is in accordance with what we now know respecting the nature of heat, for when a body passes from the solid to the liquid, or from the liquid or solid to the gaseous, condition, a certain amount of work has to be done, and a corresponding amount of heat is used up in the doing of it. When the body returns to its original condition, the heat is restored, as when a heavy body falls to the ground, or a bent spring returns to its original form. Cavendish's determination of the so-called latent heat of steam was very slightly in error.

About 1760 very extraordinary beliefs were current respecting the excessive degree of cold and the rapid variations of temperature which take place in the Arctic regions. Braun, of St. Petersburg, had observed that mercury, in solidifying in the tube of a thermometer, descended through more than four hundred degrees, and it was assumed that the melting point of mercury was about 400° below Fahrenheit's zero. It then became necessary to suppose that, while the mercury in a thermometer was freezing, there was a variation of temperature to this extent, and thus these wild reports became current. Cavendish and Black independently explained the anomaly, and each suggested the same method of determining the freezing point of mercury. Cavendish, however, had a piece of apparatus prepared which he sent to Governor Hutchins, at Albany Fort, Hudson's Bay. It consisted of an outer vessel, in which the mercury was allowed to freeze, but not throughout the whole of its mass, and the bulb of the thermometer was kept immersed in the liquid metal in the interior. In this way the mercury in the thermometer was cooled down to the melting point without commencing to solidify, and the temperature was found to be between 39° and 40° below Fahrenheit's zero.

As a chemist, Cavendish is renowned for his eudiometric analysis, whereby he determined the percentage of oxygen in air with an amount of accuracy that would be creditable to a chemist of to-day, and for his discovery of the composition of water; but to the world generally he is perhaps best known by the famous "Cavendish experiment" for determining the mass, and hence the mean density, of the earth. The apparatus was originally suggested by the Rev. John Michell, but was first employed by Cavendish, who thereby determined the mean density of the earth to be 5·45. At the request of the Astronomical

Society, the investigation was afterwards taken up by Mr. Francis Baily, who, after much labour, discovered that the principal sources of error were due to radiation of heat, and consequent variation of temperature of parts of the apparatus during the experiment. To minimize the radiation and absorption, he gilded the principal portions of the apparatus and the interior of the case in which it was contained, and his results then became consistent. Cavendish had himself suggested the cause of the discrepancy, but the gilding was proposed by Principal Forbes. As a mean of many hundreds of experiments, Mr. Baily deduced for the mean density of the earth 5·6604. Cavendish's apparatus was a delicate torsion-balance, whereby two leaden balls were supported upon the extremities of a wooden rod, which was suspended by a thin wire. These balls were about two inches in diameter, and the experiment consisted in determining the deflection of the wooden arm by the attraction of two large solid spheres of lead brought very near the balls, and so situated that the attraction of each tended to twist the rod horizontally in the same direction. The force required to produce the observed deflection was calculated from the time of swing of the rod and balls when left to themselves. The force exerted upon either ball by a known spherical mass of metal, with its centre at a known distance, being thus determined, it was easy to calculate what mass, having its centre at the centre of the earth, would be required to attract one of the balls with the force with which the earth was known to attract it.

Dr. Wilson sums up Cavendish's view of life in these words:—

His theory of the universe seems to have been that it consisted *solely* of a multitude of objects which could be weighed, numbered, and measured; and the vocation to which he considered himself called was to weigh, number, and measure as many of these objects as his allotted three score years and ten would permit. This conviction biased all his doings—alike his great scientific enterprises and the petty details of his daily life. Πάντα μέτρῳ, καὶ ἀριθμῷ, καὶ σταθμῷ was his motto; and in the microcosm of his own nature he tried to reflect and repeat the subjection to inflexible rule and the necessitated harmony which are the appointed conditions of the macrocosm of God's universe.

COUNT RUMFORD.

Benjamin Thompson, like Franklin, was a native of Massachusetts, his ancestors for several generations having been yeomen in that province, and descendants of the first colonists of the Bay. In the diploma of arms granted him when he was knighted by George III., he is described as "son of Benjamin Thompson, late of the province of Massachusetts Bay, in New England, gent." He was born in the house of his grandfather, Ebenezer Thompson, at Woburn, Massachusetts, on March 26, 1753. His father died at the age of twenty-six, on November 7, 1754, leaving the infant Benjamin and his mother to the care of the grandparents. The widow married Josiah Pierce, junior, in March, 1756, and with her child, now a boy of three, went to live in a house but a short distance from her former residence.

Young Thompson appears to have received a sound elementary education at the village school. From some remarks made by him in after years to his friend, M. Pictet, it has been inferred that he did not receive very kind treatment at the hands of his stepfather. It is clear, however, that the most affectionate relationships always obtained between him and his mother, and the latter appears to have had no cause to complain of the treatment she received from her second husband, with whom she lived to a very good old age. That Thompson in early boyhood developed some tendencies which did not meet with ready sympathy from those around him is, however, equally clear. His guardians destined him for a farmer, like his ancestors, and his experiments in mechanics, which took up much of his playtime and in all probability not a few hours which should have been devoted to less interesting work, were not regarded as tending towards the end in view. Hence he was probably looked upon as "indolent, flighty, and unpromising." Later on he was sent to school in Byfield, and in 1764, at the age of eleven, "was put under the tuition of Mr. Hill, an able teacher in Medford, a town adjoining Woburn." At length, his friends having given up all hope of ever making a farmer of the boy, he was apprenticed, on October 14, 1766, to Mr. John Appleton, of Salem, an importer of British goods and dealer in miscellaneous articles. He lived with his master, and seems to have done his work in a manner satisfactory on the whole, but there is evidence that he would, during business hours, occupy his spare moments with mechanical contrivances, which he used to hide under the counter, and even ventured occasionally to practise on his fiddle in the store. He stayed with Mr. Appleton till the autumn of 1769, and during this time he attended the ministry of the Rev. Thomas Barnard. This gentleman seems to have taken great interest in the boy, and to have taught him mathematics, so that at the age of fifteen he was able "to calculate an eclipse," and was delighted when the eclipse commenced within six seconds of his calculated time. Thompson, while an apprentice, showed a great faculty for drawing and designing, and used to carve devices for his friends on the handles of their knives or other implements. It was at this time he constructed an elaborate contrivance to produce perpetual motion, and on one evening it is said that he walked from Salem to Woburn, to show it to Loammi Baldwin, who was nine years older than himself, but his most intimate friend. Like many other devices designed for the same purpose, it had only one fault—it wouldn't go.

It was in 1769, while preparing fireworks for the illumination on the abolition of the Stamp Act, that Thompson was injured by a severe explosion as he was grinding his materials in a mortar. His note-book contained many directions for the manufacture of fireworks.

During Thompson's apprenticeship those questions were agitating the public mind which finally had their outcome in the War of Independence. Mr. Appleton was one of those who signed the agreement refusing to import British goods, and this so affected the trade of the store that he had no further need for the apprentice. Hence it was that, in the autumn of 1769, Thompson went to Boston as apprentice-clerk in a dry goods store, but had to leave after a few months, through the depression in trade consequent on the non-importation agreement.

His note-book, containing the entries made at this time, comprised several comic sketches very well drawn, and a quantity of business memoranda which show that he was very systematic in keeping his accounts. His chief method of earning money, or rather of making up the "Cr." side of his accounts, was by cutting and cording wood. A series of entries made in July and August, 1771, show the expense he incurred in constructing an electrical machine. It is not easy to determine, from the list of items purchased, the character of the machine he constructed; but it is interesting to note that the price in America at that time of nitric acid was *2s. 6d.* per ounce; of lacquer, *40s.* per pint; of shellac, *5s.* per ounce; brass wire, *40s.* per pound; and iron wire, *1s. 3d.* per yard. The nature of the problems which occupied his thoughts during the last year or two of his business life are apparent in the following letters:—

Woburn, August 16, 1769.

Mr. Loammi Baldwin,

SIR,

Please to inform me in what manner fire operates upon clay to change the colour from the natural colour to red, and from red to black, etc.; and how it operates upon silver to change it to blue.

I am your most humble and obedient servant,

BENJAMIN THOMPSON

God save the king.

Woburn, August, 1769.

Mr. Loammi Baldwin,
SIR,

Please to give the nature, essence, beginning of existence, and rise of the wind in general, with the whole theory thereof, so as to be able to answer all questions relative thereto.

Yours,

BENJAMIN THOMPSON.

This was an extensive request, and the reply was probably not altogether satisfactory to the inquirer. On the back of the above letter was written:—

Woburn, August 15, 1769.

SIR

There was but few beings (for inhabitants of this world) created before the airy element was; so it has not been transmitted down to us how the Great Creator formed the matter thereof. So I shall leave it till I am asked only the Natural Cause, and why it blows so many ways in so short a time as it does.

Thompson appears now to have given up business and commenced the study of medicine under Dr. Hay, to whom for a year and a half he paid forty shillings per week for his board. During this time he paid part of his expenses by keeping school for a few weeks consecutively at Wilmington and Bradford, and another part was paid by cords of wood. His business capacity, as well as his dislike of ordinary work, is shown by some arrangements which he made for getting wood cut and corded at prices considerably below those at which he was himself paid for it. His note-book made at this time contains, besides business entries, several receipts for medicines and descriptions of surgical operations, in some cases illustrated by sketches. In his work he was methodical and industrious, and the life of a medical student suited his genius far better than that of a clerk in a dry goods store. When teaching at

Wilmington he seems to have attracted attention by the gymnastic performances with which he exercised both himself and his pupils. While a student with Dr. Hay, he attended some of the scientific lectures at Harvard College. The pleasure and profit which he derived from these lectures are sufficiently indicated by the fact that forty years afterwards he made the college his residuary legatee.

Thompson won such a reputation as a teacher during the few weeks that he taught in village schools in the course of his student life, that he received an invitation from Colonel Timothy Walker to come to Concord, in New Hampshire, on the Merrimack, and accept a permanent situation in a higher grade school. It was from this place that he afterwards took his title, for the early name of Concord was Rumford, and the name was changed to Concord "to mark the restoration of harmony after a long period of agitation as to its provincial jurisdiction and its relation with its neighbours."

The young schoolmaster of Concord was soon on very intimate terms with the minister of the town, the Rev. Timothy Walker,[5] a man who was so much respected that he had thrice been sent to Britain on diplomatic business. Mr. Walker's daughter had been married to Colonel Rolfe, a man of wealth and position, and, with the exception of the Governor of Portsmouth, said to have been the first man in New Hampshire to drive a curricle and pair of horses. Thompson soon married—or, as he told Pictet, was married to—the young widow. Whatever may have been implied by this other way of putting the question, there is no doubt that Thompson always had the greatest possible respect for his father-in-law, and ever remembered him with sincere gratitude. The fortunes of the gallant young schoolmaster now appeared to be made; when the engagement was settled, the carriage and pair were brought out again, and the youth was attired in his favourite scarlet as a man of wealth and position. In this garb he drove to Woburn, and introduced his future wife to his mother, whose surprise can be better imagined than described.

[5] Father of the colonel.

The exact date of Thompson's marriage is not known. His daughter Sarah, afterwards Countess of Rumford, was born in the Rolfe mansion on October 18, 1774. It is needless to say that the engagement to Mrs. Rolfe terminated the teaching at the school.

Thompson now had a large estate and ample means to improve it. He gave much attention to gardening, and sent to England for garden seeds. In some way he attracted the attention of Governor Wentworth, the Governor of Portsmouth, who invited him to the Government House, and was so taken with the former apprentice, medical student, and schoolmaster, that he gave him at once a commission as major. This appointment was the cause of the misfortunes which almost immediately began to overtake him. He incurred the jealousy of his fellow-officers, over whom he had been appointed, and he failed to secure the confidence of the civilians of Concord.

Public feeling in New England was very much excited against the mother country. Representations were sent to the British Government, but appeared to be treated with contempt. Very many of these documents were found, after the war was over, unopened in drawers at the Colonial Office. British ministers appeared to know little about the needs of their American dependencies, and relations rapidly became more and more strained. The patriots appointed committees to watch over the patriotism of their fellow-townsmen, and thus the freedom of a free country was inaugurated by an institution bordering in character very closely upon the Inquisition; and the Committees of Correspondence and Safety accepted evidence from every spy or eavesdropper who came before them with reports of suspected persons. Thompson was accused of "Toryism;" the only definite charge against him being that he had secured remission of punishment for some deserters from Boston who had for some time worked upon his estate. He was summoned before the Committee of Safety, but refused to make any confession of acts injurious to his country, on the ground that he had nothing to confess. His whole after-life shows that his sympathies were very much on the side of monarchy and centralization, but at this time there appears to have been no evidence that could be brought against him. The populace, however, stormed his house, and he owed his safety to the fact that he had received notice of their intentions, and had made his escape a few hours before. This was in November, 1774. Thompson then took refuge at Woburn, with his mother, but the popular ill feeling troubled him here, so that his life was one of great anxiety.

While at Woburn, his wife and child joined him, and stayed there for some months. At length he was arrested and confined in the town upon suspicion of being inimical to the interests of his country. When he was brought before the Committee of Inquiry, there was no evidence brought against him. Major Thompson then petitioned to be heard before the Committee of the Provincial Congress at Washington. This petition he entrusted to his friend Colonel Baldwin to present. The petition was referred by the committee to Congress, by whom it was deferred for the sake of more pressing business. At length he secured a hearing in his native town, but the result was indecisive, and he did not obtain the public acquittal that he desired, though the Committee of Correspondence found that the "said Thompson" had not "in any one instance shown a disposition unfriendly to American liberty; but that his general behaviour has evinced the direct contrary; and as he has now given us the strongest assurances of his good intentions, we recommend him to the friendship, confidence, and protection of all good people in this and the neighbouring provinces." This decision, however, does not appear to have been made public; and Thompson, on his release, retired to Charlestown, near Boston. When the buildings of Harvard College were converted into barracks, Major Thompson assisted in the transfer of the books to Concord. It is said that, after the battle of Charlestown, Thompson was introduced to General Washington, and would probably have received a commission under him but for the opposition of some of the New Hampshire officers. He afterwards took refuge in Boston, and it does not appear that he ever again saw his wife or her father. His daughter he did not see again till 1796, when she was twenty-two years of age. On March 24, 1776, General Washington obliged the British troops to evacuate Boston; Thompson was the first official bearer of this intelligence to London. Of course, his property at Concord was confiscated to the commonwealth of Massachusetts, and he himself was proscribed in the Alienation Act of New Hampshire, in 1778.

When Thompson reached London with the intelligence of the evacuation of Boston, Lord George Germaine, the Secretary for War, saw that he could afford much information which would be of value to the Government. An appointment was soon found for him in the Colonial Office, and afterwards he was made Secretary of the Province of Georgia, in which latter capacity, however, he had no duties to fulfil. Throughout his career in the Colonial Office he remained on very intimate terms with Lord George Germaine, and generally breakfasted with him. In July, 1778, he was guest of Lord George at Stoneland Lodge, and here, in company with Mr. Ball, the Rector of Withyham, he undertook experiments "to determine the most advantageous situation for the vent in firearms, and to measure the velocities of bullets and the recoil under various circumstances."

The results of these investigations procured for him the friendship of Sir Joseph Banks, the President of the Royal Society, and Thompson was not the man to lose opportunities for want of making use of them. In 1779 he was elected a Fellow of the Royal Society, "as a gentleman well versed in natural knowledge and many branches of polite learning." In the same year he went for a cruise in the *Victory* with Sir Charles Hardy, in order to pursue his experiments on gunpowder with heavy guns. Here he studied the principles of naval artillery, and devised a new code of marine signals. In 1780 he was made Under-Secretary of State for the Northern Department, and in that capacity had the oversight of the transport and commissariat arrangements for the British forces.

On the defeat of Cornwallis, Lord George Germaine and his department had to bear the brunt of Parliamentary dissatisfaction. Lord George resigned his position in the Government, and was created Viscount Sackville. He had, however, previously conferred on Thompson a commission as lieutenant-colonel in the British army, and Thompson, probably foreseeing the outcome of events and its effect on the Ministry, was already in America when Lord George resigned. He had intended landing at New York, but contrary winds drove him to Charlestown. It is needless to trace the sad events which preceded the end of the war. It was to be expected that many bitter statements would be made by his countrymen respecting Thompson's own actions as colonel commanding a British garrison, for at length he succeeded in reaching Long Island, and taking the command of the King's American Dragoons, who were there awaiting him. The spirit of war always acts injuriously on those exposed to its influence, and Lieutenant-Colonel Thompson in Long Island was doubtless a very different man from that which we find him to have been before and after; nor were the months so spent very fruitful in scientific work.

In 1783, before the final disbanding of the British forces, Thompson returned to England, and was promoted to the rank of colonel, with half-pay for the rest of his life. Still anxious for military service, he obtained permission to travel on the Continent, in hopes of serving in the Austrian army against the Turks. He took with him three English horses, which rendered themselves very objectionable to his fellow-travellers while crossing the Channel in a small boat. Thompson went to Strasbourg, where he attracted the attention of the Prince Maximilian, then Field-Marshal of France, but afterwards Elector of Bavaria. On leaving Strasbourg, the prince gave him an introduction to his uncle, the Elector of Bavaria. He stayed some days at Munich, but on reaching Vienna learned that the war against the Turks would not be carried on, so he returned to Munich, and thence to England.

M. Pictet gives the following as Rumford's account of the manner in which he was cured of his passion for war:—

"'I owe it,' said he to me, one day, 'to a beneficent Deity, that I was cured in season of this martial folly. I met, at the house of the Prince de Kaunitz, a lady, aged seventy years, of infinite spirit and full of information. She was the wife of General Bourghausen. The emperor, Joseph II., came often to pass the evening with her. This excellent person conceived a regard for me; she gave me the wisest advice, made my ideas take a new direction, and opened my eyes to other kinds of glory than that of victory in battle.'"

If the course in life which Colonel Thompson afterwards took was due to the advice of this lady, she deserves a European reputation. The Elector of Bavaria, Charles Theodore, gave Thompson a pressing invitation to enter his service in a sort of semi-military and semi-civil capacity, to assist in reorganizing his dominions and removing the abuses which had crept in.

Before accepting this appointment, it was necessary to obtain the permission of George III. The king not only approved of the arrangement, but on February 23, 1784, conferred on the colonel the honour of knighthood. Sir Benjamin then returned to Bavaria, and was appointed by the elector colonel of a regiment of cavalry and general aide-de-camp. A palatial residence in Munich was furnished for him, and here he lived more as a prince than a soldier. It was eleven years before he returned, even on a visit, to England, and these years were spent by him in works of philanthropy and statesmanship, to which it is difficult to find a parallel. At one time he is found reorganizing the military system of the country, arranging a complete system of military police, erecting arsenals at Mannheim and Munich; at another time he is carrying out scientific investigations in one of these arsenals; and then he is cooking cheap dinners for the poor of the country.

One great evil of a standing army is the idleness which it develops in its members, unfitting them for the business of life when their military service is ended. Thompson commenced by attacking this evil. In 1788 he was made major-general of cavalry and Privy Councillor of State, and was put at the head of the War Department, with instructions to carry out any schemes which he had developed for the reform of the army and the removal of mendicity. Four years after his arrival in Munich he began to put some of his plans into operation. The pay of the soldiers was only threepence per day, and their quarters extremely uncomfortable, while their drill and discipline were unnecessarily irksome. Thompson set to work to make "soldiers citizens and citizens soldiers." The soldier's pay, uniform, and quarters were improved; the discipline rendered less irksome; and schools in which the three R's were taught were connected with all the regiments,—and here not only the soldiers, but their children as well as other children, were taught gratuitously. Not only were the soldiers employed in public works, and thus accustomed to habits of industry, while they were enlivened in their work by the strains of their own military bands, but they were supplied with raw material of various kinds, and allowed, when not on duty, to manufacture various articles and sell them for their own benefit—an arrangement which in this country to-day would probably raise a storm of opposition from the various trades. The garrisons were made permanent, so that soldiers might all be near their homes and remain there, and in time of peace only a small portion of the force was required to be in garrison at any time, so that the great part of his life was spent by each soldier at home. Each soldier had a small garden appropriated to his use, and its produce was his sole property. Garden seeds, and especially seed potatoes, were provided for the men, for at that time the potato was almost unknown in Bavaria. Under these circumstances a reform was quickly effected; idle men began to take interest in their gardens, and all looked on Sir

Benjamin as a benefactor.

Having thus secured the co-operation of the army, Thompson determined to attack the mendicants. The number of beggars may be estimated from the fact that in Munich, with a population of sixty thousand, no less than two thousand six hundred beggars were seized in a week. In the towns, they possessed a complete organization, and positions of advantage were assigned in regular order, or inherited according to definite customs. In the country, farm labourers begged of travellers, and children were brought up to beggary from their infancy. Of course, the evils did not cease with simple begging. Children were stolen and ill treated, for the purpose of assisting in enlisting sympathy, and the people had come to regard these evils as inevitable. Thompson organized a regular system of military patrol through every village of the country, four regiments of cavalry being set apart for this work. Then on January 1, 1790, when the beggars were out in full force to keep their annual holiday, Thompson, with the other field officers and the magistrates of the city, gave the signal, and all the beggars in Munich were seized upon by the three regiments of infantry then in garrison. The beggars were taken to the town hall, and their names and addresses entered on lists prepared for the purpose. They were ordered to present themselves next day at the "military workhouse," and a committee was appointed to inquire into the condition of each, the city being divided into sixteen districts for that purpose. Relieved of an evil which they had regarded as inevitable, the townspeople readily subscribed for the purpose of affording systematic relief, while tradesmen sent articles of food and other requisites to "the relief committee." In the military workhouse the former mendicants made all the uniforms for the troops, besides a great deal of clothes for sale in Bavaria and other countries. Thompson himself fitted up and superintended the kitchen, where food was daily cooked for between a thousand and fifteen hundred persons; and, under Sir Benjamin's management, a dinner for a thousand was cooked at a cost for fuel of fourpence halfpenny—a result which has scarcely been surpassed in modern times, even at Gateshead.

That Thompson's work was appreciated by those in whose interest it was undertaken is shown by the fact that when, on one occasion, he was dangerously ill, the poor of Munich went in public procession to the cathedral to pray for him, though he was a foreigner and a Protestant. Perhaps it may appear that his philanthropic work has little to do with physical science; but with Thompson everything was a scientific experiment, conducted in a truly scientific manner. For example, the lighting of the military workhouse afforded matter for a long series of experiments, described in his papers on photometry, coloured shadows, etc. The investigations on the best methods of employing fuel for culinary purposes led to some of his most elaborate essays; and his essay on food was welcomed alike in London and Bavaria at a time of great scarcity, and when famine seemed impending.

The Emperor Joseph was succeeded by Leopold II., but during the interregnum the Elector of Bavaria was Vicar of the Empire, and he employed the power thus temporarily placed in his hands in raising Sir Benjamin to the dignity of Count of the Holy Roman Empire, with the order of the White Eagle, and the title which the new count selected was the old name of the village in New England where he had spent the two or three years of his wedded life.

In 1795 Count Rumford returned to England, in order to publish his essays, and to make known in this country something of the work in which he had been engaged. Soon after his arrival he was robbed of most of his manuscripts, the trunk containing them being stolen from his carriage in St. Paul's Churchyard. On the invitation of Lord Pelham, he visited Dublin, and carried out some of his improvements in the hospitals and other institutions of that city. On his return to London he fitted up the kitchen of the Foundling Hospital.

Lady Thompson lived to hear of her husband's high position in Bavaria, but died on January 29, 1792. When Rumford came to London in 1795, he wrote to his daughter, who was then twenty-one years of age, to meet him there, and on January 29, 1796, she started in the *Charlestown*, from Boston. She remained with her father for more than three years, and her autobiography gives much information respecting the count's doings during this time.

While in London, Count Rumford attained a high reputation as a curer of smoky chimneys. One firm of builders found full employment in carrying out work in accordance with his instructions; and in his hotel at Pall Mall he conducted experiments on fireplaces. He concluded that the sides of a fireplace ought to make an angle of 135° with the back, so as to throw the heat straight to the front; and that the width of the back should be one-third of that of the front opening, and be carried up perpendicularly till it joins the breast. The "Rumford roaster" gained a reputation not less than that earned by his open fireplace.

It was during this stay in London that Rumford presented to the Royal Society of London, and to the American Academy of Sciences £1000 Three per Cent. Stock, for the purpose of endowing a medal to be called the Rumford Medal, and to be given each alternate year for the best work done during the preceding two years in the subjects of heat and light. He directed that two medals, one in gold and the other in silver, should be struck from the same die, the value of the two together to amount to £60. Whenever no award was made, the interest was to be added to the principal, and the excess of the income for two years over £60 was to be presented in cash to the recipient of the medal. At present the amount thus presented is sufficient to pay the composition fee for life membership of the Royal Society. The first award of the medal was made in 1802, to Rumford himself. The other recipients have been John Leslie, William Murdock, Étienne-Louis Malus, William Charles Wells, Humphry Davy, David Brewster, Augustin Jean Fresnel, Macedonio Melloni, James David Forbes, Jean Baptiste Biot, Henry Fox Talbot, Michael Faraday, M. Regnault, F. J. D. Arago, George Gabriel Stokes, Neil Arnott, M. Pasteur, M. Jamin, James Clerk Maxwell, Kirchoff, John Tyndall, A. H. L. Fizeau, Balfour Stewart, A. O. des Cloiseaux, A. J. Ångström, J. Norman Lockyer, P. J. C. Janssen, W. Huggins, Captain Abney.

In the summer of 1796 Rumford and his daughter left England to return to Munich. On account of the war, they were obliged to go by sea to Hamburg; whence they drove to Munich, where the count was anxiously expected, political troubles having compelled the elector to leave the city. After the battle of Friedburg, the Austrians retired to Munich, and, finding the gates of the city closed, they fortified themselves on an eminence overlooking the city, and, through some misunderstanding with the local authorities, the Austrian general threatened to attack the city if any Frenchman should be allowed to enter. Rumford took supreme command of the Bavarian forces, and so gained the respect of the rival generals that neither the French nor the Austrians made any attempt to enter the city. The large number of soldiers now in Munich gave Rumford a good opportunity to exercise his skill in cooking on a large scale, and this he did, adding to the comfort of the soldiers and reducing the cost of the commissariat. On the return of the elector, Miss Sarah was made a countess, and one-half of her father's pension was secured to her, thus providing her with an income of about £200 per annum for life. Many of the details of the home life and social intercourse during this period of residence at Munich are preserved in the autobiography of the countess, as well as accounts of excursions, including a trip by river to Salzburg for the purpose of inspecting the salt-mines. After two years' stay in Munich, the count was appointed Minister Plenipotentiary from Bavaria to the Court of Great Britain. After an unpleasant and perilous journey, he reached London, *viâ* Hamburg, in September, 1798, but was terribly disappointed on learning that a British subject could not be accepted as an envoy from a Foreign Power. As he did not then wish to return to Bavaria, he purchased a house in Brompton Row. But he had been too much accustomed to great enterprises to be content with a quiet life, and was bound to have some important scheme on hand. Pressing invitations were sent him to return to America, but he preferred residence in London, and devoted himself to the foundation of the Royal Institution, though the countess returned to the States in August, 1799. A letter from

Colonel Baldwin to her father shortly after her return contains the following passage:—

> In the cask of fruit which your daughter and Mr. Rolfe have sent you, there is half a dozen apples of the growth of my farm, wrapped up in papers, with the name of *Baldwin's apples* written upon them.... It is (I believe) a spontaneous production of this country; that is, it was not originally engrafted fruit.

The history of the remaining period of Rumford's residence in London is the early history of the Royal Institution.

For many years Rumford had had at his disposal for his philanthropic projects all the resources of the electorate of Bavaria, and he had done everything on a royal scale. His original plan for the Royal Institution appears to embody to a very great extent the work of the Science and Art Department, the City and Guilds Institute for the Advancement of Technical Education, the National School of Cookery, the London Society for the Extension of University Teaching, and, in addition to all this, to have comprehended a sort of perpetual International Health Exhibition, where every device for domestic purposes, and especially for the improvement of the condition of the poor, could be inspected. How all this was to be carried out with the resources which the count expected to be able to devote to the purpose, does not appear. Foremost among the objects of the institution was placed the management of fire; for its promoter was convinced that more than half the fuel consumed in the country might be saved by proper arrangements.

The philanthropic objects with which the institution was started are apparent from the fact that it was the Society for Bettering the Condition of the Poor which appointed a committee to confer with Rumford, to report on the scheme, and to raise the funds necessary for starting the project; and one of Rumford's hopes in connection with it was "to make benevolence fashionable." It was arranged that donors of fifty guineas each should be perpetual proprietors of the institution; and that subscribers should be admitted at a subscription of two guineas per annum, or ten guineas for life. The price of a proprietor's share was raised to sixty guineas from May 1, 1800, and afterwards increased by ten guineas per annum up to one hundred guineas. In a very short time there were fifty-eight fifty-guinea subscribers, and to them Rumford addressed a pamphlet, setting forth his scheme in detail. The following are specified as some of the contents of the future institution: —"Cottage fireplaces and kitchen utensils for cottagers; a farm-house kitchen with its furnishings; a complete kitchen, with its utensils, for the house of a gentleman of fortune; a laundry, including boilers, washing, ironing, and drying rooms, for a gentleman's house, or for a public hospital; the most improved German, Swedish, and Russian stoves for heating rooms and passages." As far as possible all these things were to be seen at work. There were also to be ornamental open stoves with fires in them; working models of steam-engines, of brewers' boilers, of distillers' coppers and condensers, of large boilers for hospital kitchens, and of ships' coppers with the requisite utensils; models of ventilating apparatus, spinning-wheels and looms "adapted to the circumstances of the poor;" models of agricultural machinery and bridges, and "of all such other machines and useful instruments as the managers of the institution shall deem worthy of public notice." All articles were to be provided with proper descriptions, with the name and address of the maker, and the price.

A lecture-room and laboratory were to be fitted up with all necessary philosophical apparatus, and the most eminent expounders of science were to be engaged for the purpose of "teaching the application of science to the useful purposes of life."

The lectures were to include warming and ventilation, the preservation of food, agricultural chemistry, the chemistry of digestion, of tanning, of bleaching and dyeing, "and, in general, of all the mechanical arts as they apply to the various branches of manufacture." The institution was to be governed by nine managers, of whom three were to be elected each year by the proprietors; and there was also to be a committee of visitors, the members of which should not be the managers. The king became patron of the institution, and the first set of officers was nominated by him. The Earl of Winchelsea and Nottingham was President; the Earls of Morton and of Egremont and Sir Joseph Banks, Vice-Presidents; the Earls of Bessborough, of Egremont, and of Morton, and Count Rumford, were among the Managers; the Duke of Bridgewater, Viscount Palmerston, and Earl Spencer the Visitors; and Dr. Thomas Garnett was appointed first Professor of Physics and Chemistry. The royal charter of the institution was sealed on January 13, 1800. The superintendence of the journals of the institution was entrusted to Rumford's care. For some time the count resided in the house in Albemarle Street, which had been purchased by the institution, and while there he superintended the workmen and servants.

Dr. Thomas Garnett, the first professor at the institution, was highly respected both as a man and a philosopher, and seems to have been everywhere well spoken of. But Rumford and he could not work together, and his connection with the institution was consequently a short one. Rumford was then authorized to engage Dr. Young as Professor of Natural Philosophy, editor of the journals, and general superintendent of the house, at a salary of £300 per annum. Shortly before this the count's attention had been directed to the experiments on heat, made by Humphry Davy, and on February 16, 1801, it was "resolved that Mr. Humphry Davy be engaged in the service of the Royal Institution, in the capacity of Assistant-Lecturer in Chemistry, Director of the Chemical Laboratory, and Assistant-Editor of the Journals of the Institution; and that he be allowed to occupy a room in the house, and be furnished with coals and candles, and that he be paid a salary of one hundred guineas *per annum*." In his personal appearance, Davy is said to have been at first somewhat uncouth, and the count was by no means charmed with him at their first interview. It was not till he had heard him lecture in private that Rumford would allow Davy to lecture in the theatre of the institution; but he afterwards showed his complete confidence in the young chemist by ordering that all the resources of the institution should be at his service. Davy dined with Rumford at the count's house in Auteuil, when he visited Paris with Lady Davy and Faraday, in 1813. He commenced his duties at the institution on March 11, 1801. It was on June 15, in the same year, that the managers having objected to the syllabus of his lectures, Dr. Garnett's resignation was accepted; and on July 6 Dr. Young was appointed in his stead. Dr. Young resigned after holding the appointment only two years, as he found the duties incompatible with his work as a physician.

Rumford's life in London now became daily more unpleasant to himself. Accustomed, as he had been in Bavaria, to carry out all his projects "like an emperor," it was difficult for him to work as one member of a body of managers. One by one he quarrelled with his colleagues, and at length left England, in May, 1802, never to return.

When distinguished men of science are placed at the head of an institution like that which Rumford founded, there is always a tendency for the *technical* teaching of the establishment to become gradually merged into scientific research; and in this case, after Rumford's departure, the genius of Davy gradually converted the Royal Institution into the establishment for scientific research which it has been for more than three quarters of a century. Probably the man who has come nearest to realizing all that Count Rumford had planned for his institution is the late Sir Henry Cole; but he succeeded only through the resources of the Treasury.

On leaving England in May, 1802, Rumford went to Paris, where he stayed till July or August, when he revisited Bavaria and remained there till the following year, when he returned to Paris. He was again at Munich in 1805; but under the new elector, though an old friend of the count, relationships do not seem to have been all that they were with his uncle, and at length the elector himself was compelled to leave Munich, and soon after the Bavarian sovereign became a vassal of Napoleon. On October 24, 1805, Rumford married Madame Lavoisier, a lady of brilliant talents and ample fortune. That his position might be nearly equal to hers, the Elector of Bavaria raised his pension to £1200 per annum. A house, Rue d'Anjou, No. 39, was purchased for six thousand guineas, and Rumford expended much thought and energy in making it, with its garden of two acres, all that he could desire. But the union was not so happy as he anticipated. The count loved quiet; Madame de Rumford was fond of company: to the former the pleasure of the table had no charms; the latter took delight in sumptuous dinner-parties. As time went on, domestic affairs became more and more unpleasant, and at length a friendly separation was agreed upon, after they had lived together for about three years and a half. The count then retired to a small estate which he hired at Auteuil, about four miles from Paris. The Elector of Bavaria was crowned king on January 1, 1806, and in 1810 Rumford was again at Munich, for the purpose of forming, at the king's request, an Academy of Arts and Sciences. At Auteuil the count was joined by his daughter in December, 1811, her journey having been much delayed through the capture of the vessel in which she had taken her passage, off Bordeaux. An engraving of the house at Auteuil, and the room in which Rumford carried on his experiments, was published in the *Illustrated London News* of January 22, 1870.

While resident at Auteuil, Rumford frequently read papers before the Institute of France, of which he was a member. He complained very much of the jealousy exhibited by the other members with reference to any discoveries made by a foreigner. He died in his house at Auteuil, on August 21, 1814, in the sixty-second year of his age. In 1804 he had made over, by deed of gift to his mother, the sum of ten thousand dollars, that she might leave it by will to her younger children. As before mentioned, Harvard College was his residuary legatee, and the property so bequeathed founded the Rumford Professorship in that institution.

Cuvier, as Secretary of the Institute, pronounced the customary eulogy over its late member. The following passages throw some light on the reputation in which the count was held:—

> He has constructed two singularly ingenious instruments of his own contriving. One is a new calorimeter for measuring the amount of heat produced by the combustion of any body. It is a receptacle containing a given quantity of water, through which passes, by a serpentine tube, the product of the combustion; and the heat that is generated is transmitted through the water, which, being raised by a fixed number of degrees, serves as the basis of the calculations. The manner in which the exterior heat is prevented from affecting the experiment is very simple and very

ingenious. He begins the operation at a certain number of degrees below the outside heat, and terminates it at the same number of degrees above it. The external air takes back during the second half of the experiment exactly what it gave up during the first. The other instrument serves for noting the most trifling differences in the temperature of bodies, or in the rapidity of its changes. It consists of two glass bulbs filled with air, united by a tube, in the middle of which is a pellet of coloured spirits of wine; the slightest increase of heat in one of the bulbs drives the pellet towards the other. This instrument, which he called a thermoscope, was of especial service in making known to him the varied and powerful influence of different surfaces in the transmission of heat, and also for indicating a variety of methods for retarding or hastening at will the processes of heating and freezing....

He thought it was not wise or good to entrust to men, in the mass, the care of their own well-being. The right, which seems so natural to them, of judging whether they are wisely governed, appeared to him to be a fictitious fancy born of false notions of enlightenment. His views of slavery were nearly the same as those of a plantation-owner. He regarded the government of China as coming nearest to perfection, because, in giving over the people to the absolute control of their only intelligent men, and in lifting each of those who belonged to this hierarchy on the scale according to the degree of his intelligence, it made, so to speak, so many millions of arms the passive organs of the will of a few sound heads—a notion which I state without pretending in the slightest degree to approve it, and which, as we know, would be poorly calculated to find prevalence among European nations.

As for the rest, whatever were the sentiments of M. Rumford for men, they in no way lessened his reverence for God. He never omitted any opportunity in his works of expressing his religious admiration of Providence, and of proposing for that admiration by others, the innumerable and varied provisions which are made for the preservation of all creatures; indeed, even his political views came from his firm persuasion that princes ought to imitate Providence in this respect by taking charge of us without being amenable to us.

In front of the new Government offices and the National Museum in the Maximilian Strasse, in Munich, stand, on granite pedestals, four bronze figures, ten feet in height. These represent General Deroy, Fraunhofer, Schelling, and Count Rumford. The statue of Rumford was erected in 1867, at the king's private expense. In the English garden which Rumford planned and laid out is the monument erected during his absence in England in 1796, and bearing allegorical figures of Peace and Plenty, and a medallion of the count.

The bare enumeration of Rumford's published papers would occupy considerable space, but many of them have more to do with philanthropy and domestic economy than with physics. We have seen that, when guest of Lord George Germaine, he was engaged in experiments on gunpowder. The experiments were made in the usual manner by firing bullets into a ballistic pendulum, and recording the swing of the pendulum. Thompson suggested a modification of the ballistic pendulum, attaching the gun-barrel to the pendulum, and observing the recoil, and making allowance for the recoil due to the discharge from the gun of the products of combustion of the powder, the excess enabled the velocity of the bullet to be calculated. Afterwards he made experiments on the maximum pressure produced by the explosion of powder, and pointed out that the value of powder in ordnance does not depend simply on the whole amount of gas produced, but also on the rapidity of combustion. While superintending the arsenal at Munich, Rumford exploded small charges of powder in a specially constructed receiver, which was closed by a plug of well-greased leather, and on this was placed a hemisphere of steel pressed down by a 24-pounder brass cannon weighing 8081 pounds. He found that the weight of the gun was lifted by the explosion of quantities of powder varying from twelve to fifteen grains, and hence concluded that, if the products of combustion of the powder were confined to the space actually occupied by the solid powder, the initial pressure would exceed twenty thousand atmospheres. Rumford's calculation of the pressure, based upon the bursting of a barrel, which he had previously constructed, is not satisfactory, inasmuch as he takes no account of the fact that the inner portions of the metal would give way long before the outer layers exerted anything like their maximum tension. When a hollow vessel with thick walls, such as a gun-barrel or shell, is burst by gaseous pressure from within, the inner layers of material are stretched to their breaking tension before they receive much support from the outer layers; a rift is thus made in the interior, into which the gas enters, and the surface on which the gas presses being thus increased, the rift deepens till the fracture is complete. In order to gain the full strength due to the material employed, every portion of that material should be stretched simultaneously to the extent of its maximum safe load. This principle was first practically adopted by Sir W. G. Armstrong, who, by building up the breech of the gun with cylinders shrunk on, and so arranged that the tension increased towards the exterior, availed himself of nearly the whole strength of the metal employed to resist the explosion. Had Rumford's barrel been constructed on this principle, he would have obtained a much more satisfactory result.

These investigations were followed by a very interesting series of experiments on the conducting power of fluids for heat, and, although he pushed his conclusions further than his experiments warranted, he showed conclusively that convection currents are the principal means by which heat is transferred through the substance of fluids, and described how, when a vessel of water is heated, there is generally an ascending current in the centre, and a descending current all round the periphery. Hence it is only when a liquid expands by increase of temperature that a large mass can be readily heated from below. Water below 39° Fahr. contracts when heated. Rumford, in his paper, enlarges on the bearing of this fact on the economy of the universe, and the following extracts afford a good specimen of his style, and justify some of the statements made by Cuvier in his eulogy:—

I feel the danger to which a mortal exposes himself who has the temerity to undertake to explain the designs of Infinite Wisdom. The enterprise is adventurous, but it cannot surely be improper.

The wonderful simplicity of the means employed by the Creator of the world to produce the changes of the seasons, with all the innumerable advantages to the inhabitants of the earth which flow from them, cannot fail to make a very deep and lasting impression on every human being whose mind is not degraded and quite callous to every ingenuous and noble sentiment; but the further we pursue our inquiries respecting the constitution of the universe, and the more attentively we examine the effects produced by the various modifications of the active powers which we perceive, the more we shall be disposed to admire, adore, and love that great First Cause which brought all things into existence.

Though winter and summer, spring and autumn, and all the variety of the seasons are produced in a manner at the same time the most simple and the most stupendous (by the inclination of the axis of the earth to the plane of the ecliptic), yet this mechanical contrivance alone would not have been sufficient (as I shall endeavour to show) to produce that gradual change of temperature in the various climates which we find to exist, and which doubtless is indispensably necessary to the preservation of animal and vegetable life....

But in very cold countries the ground is frozen and covered with snow, and all the lakes and rivers are frozen over in the very beginning of winter. The cold then first begins to be extreme, and there appears to be no source of heat left which is sufficient to moderate it in any sensible degree.

Let us see what must have happened if things had been left to what might be called their natural course—if the condensation of water, on being deprived of its heat, had followed the law which we find obtains in other fluids, and even in water itself in some cases, namely, when it is mixed with certain bodies.

Had not Providence interfered on this occasion in a manner which may well be considered *miraculous*, all the fresh water within the polar circle must inevitably have been frozen to a very great depth in one winter, and every plant and tree destroyed; and it is more than probable that the region of eternal frost would have spread on every side from the poles, and, advancing towards the equator, would have extended its dreary and solitary reign over a great part of what are now the most fertile and most inhabited climates of the world!...

Let us with becoming diffidence and awe endeavour to see what the means are which have been employed by an almighty and benevolent God to protect His fair creation.

He then goes on to explain how large bodies of water are prevented from freezing at great depths on account of the expansion which takes place on cooling below 39° Fahr., and the further expansion which occurs on freezing, and mentions that in the Lake of Geneva, at a depth of a thousand feet, M. Pictet found the temperature to be 40° Fahr.

"We cannot sufficiently admire the simplicity of the contrivance by which all this heat is saved. It well deserves to be compared with that by which the seasons are produced; and I must think that every candid inquirer who will begin by divesting himself of all unreasonable prejudice will agree with me in attributing them both TO THE SAME AUTHOR...."

"But I must take care not to tire my reader by pursuing these speculations too far. If I have persisted in them, if I have dwelt on them with peculiar satisfaction and complacency, it is because I think them uncommonly interesting, and also because I conceived that they might be of value in this age of *refinement* and *scepticism*.

"If, among barbarous nations, the *fear of a God*, and the practice of religious duties, tend to soften savage dispositions, and to prepare the mind for all those sweet enjoyments which result from peace, order, industry, and friendly intercourse; a *belief in the existence of a Supreme Intelligence*, who rules and governs the universe with wisdom and goodness, is not less essential to the happiness of those who, by cultivating their mental powers, HAVE LEARNED TO KNOW HOW LITTLE CAN BE KNOWN."

Rumford, in connection with his experiments on the conducting power of liquids, tried the effect of increasing the viscosity of water by the addition of starch, and of impeding its movements by the introduction of eider-down, on the rate of diffusion of heat through it. Hence he explained the inequalities of temperature which may obtain in a mass of thick soup—inequalities which had once caused him to burn his mouth—and, applying the same principles to air, he at once turned his conclusions to practical account in the matter of warm clothing.

After an attempt to determine, if possible, the weight of a definite quantity of heat—an attempt in which very great precautions were taken to exclude disturbing causes, while the balance employed was capable of indicating one-millionth part of the weight of the body weighed—Rumford, finding no sensible effect on the balance, concluded that "if the weight of gold is neither augmented nor lessened by *one-millionth part*, upon being heated from the point of *freezing water* to that of a *bright red heat*, I think we may very safely conclude that ALL ATTEMPTS TO DISCOVER ANY EFFECT OF HEAT UPON THE APPARENT WEIGHTS OF BODIES WILL BE FRUITLESS." The theoretical investigations of Principal Hicks, based on the vortex theory of matter and the dynamical theory of heat, have recently led him to the conclusion that the attraction of gravitation may depend to some extent on temperature.

A series of very valuable experiments on the radiating powers of different surfaces showed how that power varied with the nature of the surface, and the effect of a coating of lamp-black in increasing the radiating power of a body. In order to determine the effect of radiation in the cooling of bodies, Rumford employed the thermoscope referred to by Cuvier. The following passage is worthy of attention, as the truth it expounds in the last thirteen words appears to have been but very imperfectly recognized many years after it was written:

—

"All the heat which a hot body loses when it is exposed in the air to cool is not given off to the air which comes into contact with it, but ... a large proportion of it escapes in rays, which do not heat the transparent air through which they pass, but, like light, generate heat only when and where they are stopped and absorbed."

Rumford then investigated the absorption of heat by different surfaces, and established the law that good radiators are good absorbers; and recommended that vessels in which water is to be heated should be blackened on the outside. In speculating on the use of the colouring matter in the skin of the negro, he shows his fondness for experiment:—

"All I will venture to say on the subject is that, were I called to inhabit a very hot country, nothing should prevent me from making the experiment of blackening my skin, or at least, of wearing a black shirt, in the shade, and especially at night, in order to find out if, by those means, I could contrive to make myself more comfortable."

In his experiments on the conduction of heat, Rumford employed a cylinder with one end immersed in boiling water and the other in melting ice, and determined the temperature at different points in the length of the cylinder. He found the difficulty which has recently been forcibly pointed out by Sir Wm. Thomson, in the article "Heat," in the "Encyclopædia Britannica," viz. that the circulation of the water was not sufficiently rapid to keep the temperature of the layer in contact with the metal the same as that of the rest of the water; and he also called attention to the arbitrary character of thermometer-scales, and recommended that more attention should be given to the scale of the air thermometer. It was in his visit to Edinburgh, in 1800, that, in company with some of the university professors, the count conducted some experiments in the university laboratory on the apparent radiation of cold. Rumford's views respecting *frigorific rays* have not been generally accepted, and Prevost's theory of exchanges completely explains the apparent radiation of cold without supposing that cold is anything else than the mere absence of heat.

We must pass over Rumford's papers on the use of steam as a vehicle of heat, on new boilers and stoves for the purpose of economizing fuel, and all the papers bearing on the nutritive value of different foods. The calorimeter with which he determined the amount of heat generated by the combustion, and the latent heat of evaporation, of various bodies has been already alluded to. Of the four volumes of Rumford's works published by the American Academy of Arts and Sciences, the third is taken up entirely with descriptions of fireplaces and of cooking utensils.

Before deciding on the best way to light the military workhouse at Munich, Rumford made a series of experiments on the relative economy of different methods, and for this purpose designed his well-known shadow-photometer. In the final form of this instrument the shadows were thrown on a plate of ground glass covered with paper, forming the back of a small box, from which all extraneous light was excluded. Two rods were placed in front of this screen, and the lights to be compared were so situated that the shadow of one rod thrown by the first light might be just in contact with that of the other rod thrown by the second light. By introducing coloured glasses in front of the lights, Rumford compared the illuminating powers of different sources with respect to light of a particular colour. The complementary tints exhibited by the shadows caused him to devise his theory of the harmony of complementary colours. One result is worthy of mention: it is a conclusion to which public attention has since been called in connection with "duplex" burners. Rumford found that with wax tapers the amount of light emitted per grain of wax consumed diminished with the diminution of the consumption, so that a small taper gave out only one-sixteenth as much light as an ordinary candle for the same consumption of wax. He says:—

"This result can be easily explained if we admit the hypothesis which supposes light to be analogous to sound.... The particles ... were so rapidly cooled ... that they had hardly time to shine one instant before they became too cold to be any longer visible."

An argand lamp, when compared with a lamp having a flat wick, gave more light in the ratio of 100 to 85 for the same consumption of oil.

One of the latest investigations of Rumford was that bearing on the effect of the width of the wheels on the draught of a carriage. To his own carriage, weighing, with its passengers, nearly a ton, he fitted a spring dynamometer by means of a set of pulleys attached to the under-carriage and the splinter-bar. He used three sets of wheels, respectively 1-3/4, 2-1/4, and 4 inches wide, and, introducing weights into the carriage to make up for the difference in the weights of the wheels, he found a very sensible diminution in the tractive force required as the width of the wheels was increased, and in a truly scientific spirit, despising the ridicule cast upon him, he persisted in riding about Paris in a carriage with four-inch tyres.

But the piece of work by which Rumford will be best known to future generations is that described in his paper entitled "An Inquiry concerning the Source of the Heat which is excited by Friction." It was while superintending the boring of cannon in the arsenal at Munich that Rumford was struck with the enormous amount of heat generated by the friction of the boring-bar against the metal. In order to determine whether the heat had come from the chips of metal themselves, he took a quantity of the abraded borings and an equal weight of chips cut from the metal with a fine saw, and, heating them to the temperature of boiling water, he immersed them in equal quantities of water at $59\text{-}1/2°$ Fahr. The change of temperature of the water was the same in both cases, and Rumford found that there was no change which he could discover *in regard to its capacity for heat* produced in the metal by the action of the borer.

In order to prevent the honeycombing of the castings by the escaping gas, the cannon were cast in a vertical position with the breech at the bottom of the mould and a short cylinder projecting about two feet beyond the muzzle of the gun, so that any imperfections in the casting would appear in this projecting cylinder. It was on one of these pieces of waste metal, while still attached to the gun, that Rumford conducted his experiments. Having turned the cylinder, he cut away the metal in front of the muzzle until the projecting piece was connected with the gun by a narrow cylindrical neck, $2\cdot2$ inches in diameter and 3·8 inches long. The external diameter of the cylinder was 7·75 inches, and its length 9·8 inches, and it was bored to a depth of 7·2 inches, the diameter of the bore being 3·7 inches. The cannon was mounted in the boring-lathe, and a blunt borer pressed by a screw against the bottom of the bore with a force equal to the weight of 10,000 pounds. A small transverse hole was made in the cylinder near its base for the introduction of a thermometer. The cylinder weighed 113·13 pounds, and, with the gun, was turned at the rate of thirty-two revolutions per minute by horse-power. To prevent loss of heat, the cylinder was covered with flannel. After thirty minutes' work, the thermometer, when introduced into the cylinder, showed a temperature of 130° Fahr. The loss of heat during the experiment was estimated from observations of the rate of cooling of the cylinder. The weight of metal abraded was 837 grains, while the amount of heat produced was sufficient to raise nearly five pounds of ice-cold water to the boiling point.

To exclude the action of the air, the cylinder was closed by an air-tight piston, but no change was produced in the result. As the air had access to the metal where it was rubbed by the piston, and Rumford thought this might possibly affect the result, a deal box was constructed, with slits at each end closed by sliding shutters, and so arranged that it could be placed with the boring bar passing through one slit and the narrow neck connecting the cylinder with the gun through the other slit, the sliding shutters, with the help of collars of oiled leather, serving to make the box water-tight. The box was then filled with water and the lid placed on. After turning for an hour the temperature was raised from 60° to 107° Fahr., after an hour and a half it was 142° Fahr., at the end of two hours the temperature was 178° Fahr., at two hours and twenty minutes it was 200° Fahr., and at two hours and thirty minutes it ACTUALLY BOILED!

"It would be difficult to describe the surprise and astonishment expressed in the countenances of the bystanders on seeing so large a quantity of cold water heated and actually made to boil without any fire.

"Though there was, in fact, nothing that could justly be considered as surprising in this event, yet I acknowledge fairly that it afforded me a degree of childish pleasure which, were I ambitious of the reputation of a *grave philosopher*, I ought most certainly rather to hide than to discover."

Rumford estimated the "total quantity of ice-cold water which, with the heat actually generated by the friction and accumulated in two hours and thirty minutes, might have been heated 180 degrees, or made to boil" at 26·58 pounds, and the rate of production he considered exceeded that of nine wax candles, each consuming ninety-eight grains of wax per hour, while the work of turning the lathe could easily have been performed by one horse. This was the first rough attempt ever made, so far as we know, to determine the mechanical equivalent of heat.

In his reflections on these experiments, Rumford writes:—

It is hardly necessary to add that anything which any *insulated* body or system of bodies can continue to furnish *without limitation* cannot possibly be *a material substance*; and it appears to me to be extremely difficult, if not quite impossible, to form any distinct idea of anything capable of being excited and communicated in the manner the heat was excited and communicated in these experiments, except it be MOTION.

It has been stated that, if Rumford had dissolved in acid the borings and the sawn strips of metal, the capacity for heat of which he determined, and had shown that the heat developed in the solution was the same in the two cases, his chain of argument would have been absolutely complete. Considering the amount of heat produced in the experiments, there are few minds whose conviction would be strengthened by this experiment, and it is only those who look for faultless logic that will refuse to Rumford the credit of having established the dynamical nature of heat.

Davy afterwards showed that two pieces of ice could be melted by being rubbed against one another in a vacuum, but he does not appear to have made as much as he might of the experiment. Mayer calculated the mechanical equivalent of heat from the heat developed in the compression of air, but he *assumed*, what afterwards was shown by Joule to be nearly true, that the whole of the work done in the compression was converted into heat. It was Joule, however, who first showed that heat and mechanical energy are mutually convertible, so that each may be expressed in terms of the other, a *given* quantity of heat always corresponding to the *same amount* of mechanical energy, whatever may be the intermediate stages through which it passes, and that we may therefore define the mechanical equivalent of heat as *the number of units of energy which, when entirely converted into heat, will raise unit mass of water one degree from the freezing point.*

THOMAS YOUNG.

"We here meet with a man altogether beyond the common standard, one in whom natural endowment and sedulous cultivation rivalled each other in the production of a true philosopher; nor do we hesitate to state our belief that, since Newton, Thomas Young stands unrivalled in the annals of British science." Such was the verdict of Principal Forbes on one who may not only be regarded as one of the founders of the undulatory theory of light, but who was among the first to apply the theory of elasticity to the strength of structures, while it is to him that we are indebted in the first instance for all we know of Egyptian hieroglyphics, and for the vast field of antiquarian research which the interpretation of these symbols has opened up.

Thomas Young was the son of Thomas and Sarah Young, and the eldest of ten children. His mother was a niece of the well-known physician, Dr. Richard Brocklesby, and both his father and mother were members of the Society of Friends, in whose principles all their children were very carefully trained. It was to the independence of character thus developed that Dr. Young attributed very much of the success which he afterwards attained. He was born at Milverton, in Somersetshire, on June 13, 1773. For the greater part of the first seven years of his life he lived with his maternal grandfather, Mr. Robert Davis, at Minehead, in Somersetshire. According to his own account, he could read with considerable fluency at the age of *two*, and, under the instructions of his aunt and a village schoolmistress, he had "read the Bible twice through, and also Watts's Hymns," before he attained the age of four. It may with reason be thought that both the schoolmistress and the aunt should have been severely reprimanded, and it is certain that their example is not to be commended; but Young's infantile constitution seems to have been proof against over-pressure, and before he was five years old he could recite the whole of Goldsmith's "Deserted Village," with scarcely a mistake. He commenced learning Latin before he was six, under the guidance of a Nonconformist minister, who also taught him to write. When not quite seven years of age he went to boarding-school, where he remained a year and a half; but he appears to have learned more by independent effort than under the guidance of his master, for privately he "had mastered the last rules of Walkinghame's 'Tutor's Assistant'" before reaching the middle of the book under the master's inspection. After leaving this school, he lived at home for six months, but frequently visited a neighbour who was a land surveyor, and at whose house he amused himself with philosophical instruments and scientific books, especially a "Dictionary of Arts and Sciences." When nearly nine he went to the school of Mr. Thompson, at Compton, in Dorsetshire, where he remained nearly four years, and read several Greek and Latin authors, as well as the elements of natural philosophy—the latter in books lent him by Mr. Jeffrey, the assistant-master. This Mr. Jeffrey appears to have been something of a mechanical genius, and he gave Young lessons in turning, drawing, bookbinding, and the grinding and preparation of colours. Before leaving this school, at the age of thirteen, Young had read six chapters of the Hebrew Bible.

During the school holidays the construction of a microscope occupied considerable time, and the reading of "Priestley on Air" turned Young's attention to the subject of chemistry. Having learned a little French, he succeeded, with the help of a schoolfellow, in gaining an elementary knowledge of Italian. After leaving school, he lived at home for some time, and devoted his energies mainly to Hebrew and to turning and telescope-making; but Eastern languages received a share of attention, and by the time he was fourteen he had read most of Sir William Jones's "Persian Grammar." He then went to Youngsbury, in Hertfordshire, and resided at the house of Mr. David Barclay, partly as companion and partly as classical tutor to Mr. Barclay's grandson, Hudson Gurney. This was the beginning of a friendship which lasted for life. Gurney was about a year and a half junior to Young, and for five years the boys studied together, reading the classical works which Young had previously studied at school. Before the end of these five years Young had gained more or less acquaintance with fourteen languages; but his studies were for a time delayed through a serious illness when he was little more than sixteen. To this illness his uncle, Dr. Brocklesby, referred in a letter, of which the following extract is interesting for several reasons:—

Recollect that the least slip (as who can be secure against error?) would in you, who seem in all things to set yourself above ordinary humanity, seem more monstrous or reprehensible than it might be in the generality of mankind. Your prudery about abstaining from the use of sugar on account of the negro trade, in any one else would be altogether ridiculous, but as long as the whole of your mind keeps free from spiritual pride or too much presumption in your facility of acquiring language, which is no more than the dross of knowledge, you may be indulged in such whims, till your mind becomes enlightened with more reason. My late excellent friend, Mr. Day, the author of 'Sandford and Merton,' abhorred the base traffic in negroes' lives as much as you can do, and even Mr. Granville Sharp, one of the earliest writers on the subject, has not done half as much service in the business as Mr. Day in the above work. And yet Mr. Day devoured daily as much sugar as I do; for he reasonably concluded that so great a system as the sugar-culture in the West Indies, where sixty millions of British property are employed, could never be affected either way by one or one hundred in the nation debarring themselves the reasonable use of it. Reformation must take its rise elsewhere, if ever there is a general mass of public virtue sufficient to resist such private interests. Read Locke with care, for he opens the avenues of knowledge, though he gives too little himself.

With respect to the sugar, no doubt very much may be said on Young's side of the question. It appears, however, that in his early manhood there was a good deal in his conduct which to-day would be regarded as *priggish*, though it was somewhat more in harmony with the spirit of his time.

He left Youngsbury at the age of nineteen, having read, besides his classical authors, the whole of Newton's "Principia" and "Opticks," and the systems of chemistry by Lavoisier and Nicholson, besides works on botany, medicine, mineralogy, and other scientific subjects. One of Young's peculiarities was the extraordinary neatness of his handwriting, and a translation in Greek iambics of Wolsey's farewell to Cromwell, which he sent, written very neatly on vellum, to his uncle, Dr. Brocklesby, attracted the attention of Mr. Burke, Dr. Charles Burney, and other classical scholars, so that when, a few months later, Young went to stay with his uncle in London, and was thrown into contact with some of the chief literary men of the day, he found that his fame as a scholar had preceded him. This neatness of his handwriting and his power of drawing were of great use in his researches on the Egyptian hieroglyphics. He had little faith in natural genius, but believed that anything could be accomplished by persevering application.

> "Thou say'st not only skill is gained,
> But genius too may be obtained,
>   By studious imitation."

In the autumn of 1792 Young went to London for the purpose of studying medicine. He lived in lodgings in Westminster, and attended the Hunterian School of Anatomy. A year afterwards he entered St. Bartholomew's Hospital as a medical student. The notes which he took of the lectures were written sometimes in Latin, interspersed with Greek quotations, and not unfrequently with mathematical calculations, which may be assumed to have been made before the lecture commenced. During his school days he had paid some attention to geometrical optics, and had constructed a microscope and telescope. Now his attention was attracted to a far more delicate instrument— the eye itself. Young had learned how a telescope can be "focussed" so as to give clear images of objects more or less distant. Some such power of adjustment must be possessed by the eye, or it could never form distinct images of objects, whether at a distance of a foot or a mile. The apparently fibrous structure of the crystalline lens of the eye had been noticed and described by Leuwenhoeck; and Pemberton, a century before Young took up the subject, had suggested that the fibres were muscles, by the action of which the eye was "accommodated" for near or distant vision. In dissecting the eye of an ox Young thought he had discovered evidence confirmatory of this view, and the paper which he wrote on the subject was not only published in the "Philosophical Transactions," but secured his election as a Fellow of the Royal Society in June, 1794. This paper was important, not simply because it led to Young's election to the Royal Society, but mainly because it was his first published paper on optical subjects. Later on he showed incontestably, by exact measurements, that it is the crystalline lens which changes its form during adjustment; but he was wrong in supposing the fibres of the lens to be muscular. By carefully measuring the distance between the images of two candles formed by reflection from the cornea, he showed that the cornea experienced no change of form. His eyes were very prominent; and turning them so as to look very obliquely, he measured the length of the eye from back to front with a pair of compasses whose points were protected, pressing one point against the cornea, and the other between the back of the eye and the orbit, and showed that, when the eye was focussed for different distances, there was no change in the length of the axis. The crystalline lens was the only resource left whereby the accommodation could be effected. The accommodation is, in fact, brought about by the action of the ciliary muscle. The natural form of the lens is more convex than is consistent with distinct vision, except for very near objects. The tension of the suspensory ligament, which is attached to the front of the lens all round its edge, renders the anterior surface of the lens much less curved than it would naturally be. The ciliary muscle is a ring of muscular fibre attached to the ciliary process close to the circumference of the suspensory ligament. By its contraction it forms a smaller ring, and, diminishing the external diameter, it releases the tension of the suspensory ligament, thus allowing the crystalline lens to bulge out and adapt itself for the diverging rays coming from near objects. It is the exertion of contracting the ciliary muscle that constitutes the effort of which we are conscious when looking at very near objects. It was not, however, till long after the time of Dr. Young that this complicated action was fully made out, though the change of form of the anterior surface of the crystalline lens was discovered by the change in the image of a bright object formed by reflection.

In the spring of 1794 Young took a holiday tour in Cornwall, with Hudson Gurney, visiting on his way the Duke of Richmond, who was drinking the waters at Bath, under the advice of Dr. Brocklesby. In Cornwall, the mining machinery attracted his attention very much more than the natural beauties of the country. Towards the end of the summer he visited the Duke of Richmond at Goodwood, when the duke offered him the appointment of private secretary. He resolved, however, to continue his medical course, one of the reasons which he alleged being his regard for the Society of Friends, whose principles he considered inconsistent with the appointment of Private Secretary to the Master-General of the Ordnance.

The following winter he spent as a medical student at Edinburgh. Here he gave up the costume of the Society of Friends, and in many ways departed from their rules of conduct. He mingled freely with the university, attended the theatre, took lessons in dancing and playing the flute, and generally cultivated the habits of what is technically known as "society." Throughout this change in his life he retained his high moral principles as a guide of conduct, and appears to have acted from a firm conviction of what was right. At the same time, it must be admitted that the breaking down of barriers, however conventional they may be, is an operation attended in most cases by not a little danger. With Young, the progress of his scientific education may have been delayed on account of the new demands on his time; but besides the study of German, Spanish, and Italian, he appears to have read a considerable amount of general literature during his winter session in Edinburgh. The following summer he took a tour on horseback through the Highlands, taking with him his flute, drawing materials, spirits for preserving insects, boards for drying plants, paper and twine for packing up minerals, and a thermometer; but the geological hammer does not then appear to have been regarded as an essential to the equipment of a philosopher. At Aberdeen he stayed for three days, and reported thus on the university:—

Some of the professors are capable of raising a university to celebrity, especially Copeland and Ogilvie; but the division and proximity of the two universities (King's College and Marischal College) is not favourable to the advancement of learning; besides, the lectures are all, or mostly, given at the same hour, and the same professor continues to instruct a class for four years in the different branches. Were the colleges united, and the internal regulations of the system new modelled, the cheapness of the place, the number of small bursaries for poor or distinguished students, and the merit of the instructors, might make this university a very respectable seminary in some branches of science. The fee to a professor for a five-months' session is only a guinea and a half. I was delighted with the inspection of the rich store of mathematical and philosophical apparatus belonging to Professor Copeland of Marischal College, made in his own house, and partly with his own hands, finished with no less care than elegance; and tending to illustrate every branch of physics in the course of his lectures, which must be equally entertaining and instructive.

Before leaving the Highlands, Young visited Gordon Castle, where he stayed two days; and appears to have distinguished himself by the powers of endurance he exhibited in dancing reels. On leaving he writes: "I could almost have wished to break or dislocate a limb by chance, that I might be detained against my will; I do not recollect that I have ever passed my time more agreeably, or with a party that I thought more congenial to my own dispositions: and what would hardly be credited by many grave reasoners on life and manners, that a person who had spent the whole of his earlier years a recluse from the gay world, and a total stranger to all that was passing in the higher ranks of society, should feel himself more at home and more at ease in the most magnificent palace in the country than in the humblest dwelling with those whose birth was most similar to his own. Without enlarging on the duke's good sense and sincerity, the duchess's spirit and powers of conversation, Lady Madeline's liveliness and affability, Louisa's beauty and sweetness, Georgiana's *naïveté* and quickness of parts, young Sandy's good nature, I may say that I was truly sorry to part with every one of them."

Young seems not to have known at this time that it is an essential feature of true gentlefolk to dissipate all sense of constraint or uneasiness from those with whom they are brought into contact and that in this they can be readily distinguished from those who have wealth without breeding. The Duchess of Gordon gave Young an introduction to the Duke of Argyll, so, while travelling through the Western Highlands, he paid a visit to Inverary Castle, and "galloped over" the country with the duke's daughters. Speaking of these ladies, he says, "Lady Charlotte … is to Lady Augusta what Venus is to Minerva; I suppose she wishes for no more. Both are goddesses."

On his return to the West of England, he visited the Coalbrook Dale Iron Works, when Mr. Reynolds told him "that before the war he had agreed with a man to make a flute a hundred and fifty feet long, and two and a half in diameter, to be blown by a steam-engine and played on by barrels."

On the 7th of the following October Young left London, and after spending six days on the voyage from Yarmouth to Hamburg, he reached Göttingen on the 27th of the same month; two days afterwards he matriculated, and on November 3 he commenced his studies as a member of the university. He continued to take lessons in drawing, dancing, riding, and music, and commenced learning the clavichord. The English students at Göttingen, in order to advance their German conversation, arranged to pay a fine whenever they spoke in English in one another's company. On Sundays it was usual for the professors to give entertainments to the students, though they seldom invited them to dinner or supper. "Indeed, they could not well afford, out of a fee of a louis or two, to give large entertainments; but the absence of the hospitality which prevails rather more in Britain, is compensated by the light in which the students are regarded; they are not the less, but perhaps the more, respected for being students, and indeed, they behave in general like gentlemen, much more so than in some other German universities."

At Göttingen Young attended, in addition to his medical lectures, Spithler's lectures on the History and Constitution of the European States, Heyne on the History of the Ancient Arts, and Lichtenberg's course on Physics. Speaking of Blumenbach's lectures on Natural History, Young says, "He showed us yesterday a laborious treatise, with elegant plates, published in the beginning of this century at Wurzburg, which is a most singular specimen of credulity in affairs of natural history. Dr. Behringen used to torment the young men of a large school by obliging them to go out with him collecting petrifactions; and the young rogues, in revenge, spent a whole winter in counterfeiting specimens, which they buried in a hill which the good man meant to explore, and imposed them upon him for most wonderful *lusus naturæ*. It is interesting in a metaphysical point of view to observe how the mind attempts to accommodate itself; in one case, where the boys had made the figure of a plant thick and clumsy, the doctor remarks the difference, and says that Nature seems to have restored to the plant in thickness that which she had taken away from its other dimensions."

On April 30, 1796, Young passed the examination for his medical degree at Göttingen. The examination appears to have been entirely oral. It lasted between four and five hours. There were four examiners seated round a table provided "with cakes, sweetmeats, and wine, which helped to pass the time agreeably." They "were not very severe in exacting accurate answers." The subject he selected for his public discussion was the human voice, and he constructed a universal alphabet consisting of forty-seven letters, of which, however, very little is known. This study of sound laid the foundation, according to his own account, of his subsequent researches in the undulatory theory of light.

The autumn of 1796 Young spent in travelling in Germany; in the following February he returned to England, and was admitted a fellow-commoner of Emmanuel College, Cambridge. It is said that the Master, in introducing Young to the Tutors and other Fellows, said, "I have brought you a pupil qualified to read lectures to his tutors." Young's opinion of Cambridge, as compared with German universities, was favourable to the former; but as he had complained of the want of hospitality at Göttingen, so in Cambridge he complained of the want of social intercourse between the senior members of the university and persons *in statu pupillari*. At that time there was no system of medical education in the university, and the statutes required that six years should elapse between the admission of a medical student and his taking the degree of M.B. Young appears to have attracted comparatively little attention as an undergraduate in college. He did not care to associate with other undergraduates, and had little opportunity of intercourse with the senior members of the university. He was still keeping terms at Cambridge when his uncle, Dr. Brocklesby, died. To Young he left the house in Norfolk Street, Park Lane, with the furniture, books, pictures, and prints, and about £10,000. In the summer of 1798 a slight accident at Cambridge compelled Young to keep to his rooms, and being thus forcibly deprived of his usual round of social intercourse, he returned to his favourite studies in physics. The most important result of this study was the establishment of the principle of interference in sound, which afforded the explanation of the phenomenon of "beats" in music, and which afterwards led up to the discovery of the interference of light—a discovery which Sir John Herschel characterized as "the key to all the more abstruse and puzzling properties of light, and which would alone have sufficed to place its author in the highest rank of scientific immortality, even were his other almost innumerable claims to such a distinction disregarded."

The principle of interference is briefly this: When two waves meet each other, it may happen that their crests coincide; in this case a wave will be formed equal in height (amplitude) to the sum of the heights of the two. At another point the crest of one wave may coincide with the hollow of another, and, as the waves pass, the height of the wave at this point will be the difference of the two heights, and if the waves are equal the point will remain stationary. If a rope be hung from the ceiling of a lofty room, and the lower end receive a jerk from the hand, a wave will travel up the rope, be reflected and reversed at the ceiling, and then descend. If another wave be then sent up, the two will meet, and their passing can be observed. It will then be seen that, if the waves are exactly equal, the point at which they meet will remain at rest during the whole time of transit. If a number of waves in succession be sent up the string, the motions of the hand being properly timed, the string will appear to be divided into a number of vibrating segments separated by stationary points, or nodes. These nodes are simply the points which remain at rest on account of the upward series of waves crossing the series which have been reflected at the top and are travelling downwards. The division of a vibrating string into nodes thus affords a simple example of the principle of interference. When a tuning-fork is vibrating there are certain hyperbolic lines along which the disturbance caused by one prong is exactly neutralized by that due to the other prong. If a large tuning-fork be struck and then held near the ear and slowly turned round, the positions of comparative silence will be readily perceived. If two notes are being sounded side by side, one consisting of two hundred vibrations per second and the other of two hundred and two, then, at any distant point, it is clear that the two sets of waves will arrive in the same condition, or "phase," twice in each second, and twice they will be in opposite conditions, and, if of the same intensity, will exactly destroy one another's effects, thus producing silence. Hence twice in the second there will be silence and twice there will be sound, the waves of which have double the amplitude due to either source, and hence the sound will have four times the intensity of either note by itself. Thus there will be two "beats" per second due to interference. Later on this principle was applied by Young to very many optical phenomena of which it afforded a complete explanation.

Young completed his last term of residence at Cambridge in December, 1799, and in the early part of 1800 he commenced practice as a physician at 48, Welbeck Street. In the following year he accepted the chair of Natural Philosophy in the Royal Institution, which had shortly before been founded, and soon afterwards, in conjunction with Davy, the Professor of Chemistry, he undertook the editing of the journals of the institution. This circumstance has already been alluded to in connection with Count Rumford, the founder of the institution. He lectured at the Royal Institution for two years only, when he resigned the chair in deference to the popular belief that a physician should give his attention wholly to his professional practice, whether he has any or not. This fear lest a scientific reputation should interfere with his success as a physician haunted him for many years, and sometimes prevented his undertaking scientific work, while at other times it led him to publish anonymously the results he obtained. This anonymous publication of scientific papers caused him great trouble afterwards in order to establish his claim to his own discoveries. Many of the articles which he contributed to the supplement to the fourth, fifth, and sixth editions of the "Encyclopædia Britannica" were anonymous, although the honorarium he received for this work was increased by 25 per cent. when he would allow his name to appear. The practical withdrawal of Young from the scientific world during sixteen years was a great loss to the progress of natural philosophy, while the absence of that suavity of manner when dealing with patients which is so essential to the success of a physician, prevented him from acquiring a valuable private practice. In fact, Young was too much of a philosopher in his behaviour to succeed as a physician; he thought too deeply before giving his opinion on a diagnosis, instead of appearing to know all about the subject before he commenced his examination, and this habit, which is essential to the philosopher, does not inspire confidence in the practitioner. His fondness for society rendered him unwilling to live within the means which his uncle had left him, supplemented by what his scientific work might bring, and it was not until his income had been considerably increased by an appointment under the Admiralty that he was willing to forego the possible increase of practice which might accrue by appearing to devote his whole attention to the subject of medicine. It was this fear of public opinion which caused him, in 1812, to decline the offer of the appointment of Secretary to the Royal Society, of which, in 1802, he accepted the office of Foreign Secretary.

Young's resignation of the chair of Natural Philosophy was, however, not a great loss to the Royal Institution; for the lecture audience there was essentially of a popular character, and Young cannot be considered to have been successful as a popular lecturer. His own early education had been too much derived from private reading for him to have become acquainted with the difficulties experienced by beginners of only average ability, and his lectures, while most valuable to those who already possessed a fair knowledge of the subjects, were ill adapted to the requirements of an unscientific audience. A syllabus of his course of lectures was published by Young in 1802, but it was not till 1807 that the complete course of sixty lectures was published in two quarto volumes. They were republished in 1845 in octavo, with references and notes by Professor Kelland. Among the subjects treated in these lectures are mechanics, including strength of materials, architecture and carpentry, clocks, drawing and modelling; hydrostatics and hydraulics; sound and musical instruments; optics, including vision and the physical nature of light; astronomy; geography; the essential properties of matter; heat; electricity and magnetism; climate, winds, and meteorology generally; vegetation and animal life, and the history of the preceding sciences. The lectures were followed by a most complete bibliography of the whole subject, including works in English, French, German, Italian, and Latin. The following is the syllabus of one lecture, and illustrates the diversity of the subjects dealt with:—

"ON DRAWING, WRITING, AND MEASURING.

"Subjects preliminary to the study of practical mechanics; instrumental geometry; statics; passive strength; friction; drawing; outline; pen; pencil; chalks; crayons; Indian ink; water-colours; body colours; miniature; distemper; fresco; oil; encaustic paintings; enamel; mosaic work. Writing; materials for writing; pens; inks; use of coloured inks for denoting numbers; polygraph; telegraph; geometrical instruments; rulers; compasses; flexible rulers; squares; triangular compasses; parallel rulers; Marquois's scales; pantograph; proportional compasses; sector. Measurement of angles; theodolites; quadrants; dividing-engine; vernier; levelling; sines of angles; Gunter's scale; Nicholson's circle; dendrometer; arithmetical machines; standard measures; quotation from

Laplace; new measures; decimal divisions; length of the pendulum and of the meridian of the earth; measures of time; objections; comparison of measures; instruments for measuring; micrometrical scales; log-lines."

This represents an extensive area to cover in a lecture of one hour.

When Newton, by means of a prism,

"Unravelled all the shining robe of day,"

he showed that sunlight is made up of light varying in tint from red, through orange, yellow, green, and blue, to violet, and that by recombining all these kinds of light, or certain of them selected in an indefinite number of ways, white light could be produced. Subsequently Sir Wm. Herschel showed that rays less refrangible than the red were to be found among the solar radiation; and other rays more refrangible than the violet, but, like the ultra-red rays, incapable of exciting vision, were found by Ritter and Wollaston. In speaking of Newton's experiments, in his thirty-seventh lecture, Young says:—

It is certain that the perfect sensations of yellow and of blue are produced respectively by mixtures of red and green and of green and violet light, and there is reason to suspect that those sensations are always compounded of the separate sensations combined; at least, this supposition simplifies the theory of colours. It may, therefore, be adopted with advantage, until it be found inconsistent with any of the phenomena; and we may consider white light as composed of a mixture of red, green, and violet only, ... with respect to the quantity or intensity of the sensations produced.

It should be noticed that, in the above quotation, Young speaks only of the sensations produced. Objectively considered, sunlight consists of an infinite number of differently coloured lights comprising nearly all the shades from one end of the spectrum to the other, though white light may have a much simpler constitution, and may, for example, consist simply of a mixture of homogeneous red, green, and violet lights, or of homogeneous yellow and blue lights, properly selected. But considered subjectively, Young implies that the eye perceives three, and only three, distinct colour-sensations, corresponding to pure red, green, and violet; that when these three sensations are excited in a certain proportion, the complex sensation is that of white light; but if the relative intensities of the separate sensations differ from these ratios, the perception is that of some colour. To exhibit the effects of mixing light of different colours, Young painted differently coloured sectors on circles of cardboard, and then made the discs rotate rapidly about their centres, when the effect was the same as though the lights emitted by the sectors were mixed in proportion to the breadth of the sectors. This contrivance had been previously employed by Newton, and will be again referred to in connection with another memoir. The results of these experiments were embodied by Young in a diagram of colour, consisting of an equilateral triangle, in which the colours red, green, and violet, corresponding to the simple sensations, were placed at the angles, while those produced by mixing the primary colours in any proportions, were to be found within the triangle or along its sides; the rule being that the colour formed by the admixture of the primary colours in any proportions, was to be found at the centre of gravity of three heavy particles placed at the angular points of the triangle, with their masses proportioned to the corresponding amounts of light. Thus the colours produced by the admixture of red and green only, in different proportions, were placed along one side of the triangle, these colours corresponding to various tints of scarlet, orange, yellow, and yellowish green; another side contained the mixtures of green and violet representing the various shades of bluish green and blue; and the third side comprised the admixtures of red and violet constituting crimsons and purples. The interior of the triangle contained the colours corresponding to the mixture of all three primary sensations, the centre being neutral grey, which is a pure white faintly illuminated. If white light of a certain degree of intensity fall on white paper, the paper appears white, but if a stronger light fall on another portion of the same sheet, that which is less strongly illuminated appears grey by contrast. Shadows thrown on white paper may possess any degree of intensity, corresponding to varying shades of neutral grey, up to absolute blackness, which corresponds to a total absence of light. Thus considered, chromatically black and white are the same, differing only in the amount of light they reflect. A piece of white paper in moonlight is darker than black cloth in full sunlight.

It must be remembered that Young's diagram of colours corresponds to the admixture of coloured lights, not of colouring materials or pigments. The admixture of blue and yellow lights in proper proportions may make white or pink, but never green. The admixture of blue and yellow pigments makes a green, because the blue absorbs nearly all the light except green, blue, and a little violet, while the yellow absorbs all except orange, yellow, and green. The green light is the only light common to the two, and therefore the only light which escapes absorption when the pigments are mixed. Another point already noticed must also be carefully borne in mind. Young was quite aware that, physically, there are an infinite number of different kinds of light differing continuously in wave-length from the ultra-red to the ultra-violet, though colour can hardly be regarded as an attribute of the light considered objectively. The question of colour is essentially one of perception—a physiological, not a physical, question—and it is only in this sense that Young maintained the doctrine of three primary colours. In his paper on the production of colours, read before the Royal Society on July 1, 1802, he speaks of "the proportions of the sympathetic fibres of the retina," corresponding to these primary colour-sensations. According to this doctrine, white light would always be produced when the three sensations were affected in certain proportions, whether the exciting cause were simply two kinds of homogeneous light, corresponding to two pure tones in music, or an infinite number of different kinds, as in sunlight; and a particular yellow sensation might be excited by homogeneous yellow light from one part of the spectrum, or by an infinite number of rays of different wave-lengths, corresponding to various shades of red, orange, yellow, and green. Subjectively, the colours would be the same; objectively, the light producing them would differ exceedingly.

But Young's greatest service to science was his application of the principle of interference—of which he had already made good use in the theory of sound —to the phenomena of light. The results of these researches were presented to the Royal Society, and two of the papers were selected as Bakerian lectures in 1801 and 1803 respectively. Unfavourable criticisms of these papers, which appeared in the *Edinburgh Review*, and were said to have been written by Mr. (afterwards Lord) Brougham, seem to have caused their contents to be neglected by English men of science for many years; and it was to Arago and Fresnel that we are indebted for recalling public attention to them. The undulatory theory of light, which maintains that light consists of waves transmitted through an *ether*, which pervades all space and all matter, owes its origin to Hooke and Huyghens. Huyghens showed that this theory explained, in a very beautiful manner, the laws of reflection and of refraction, if it be allowed that light travels more slowly the denser the medium. According to the celebrated principle of Huyghens, every point in the front of a wave at any instant becomes a centre of disturbance, from which a secondary wave is propagated. The fronts of these secondary waves all lie on a surface, which becomes the new surface of the primary wave. When light enters a denser medium obliquely, the secondary waves which are propagated within the denser medium extend to a less distance than those propagated in the rarer medium, and thus the front of the primary wave becomes bent at the point where it meets the common surface. Huyghens explained, not only the laws of ordinary refraction in this manner, but, by supposing the secondary waves to form spheroids instead of spheres, he obtained the laws of refraction of the extraordinary ray in Iceland-spar. He did not, however, succeed in explaining why light should not diverge laterally instead of proceeding in straight lines. Newton supported the theory that light consists of particles or corpuscles projected in straight lines from the luminous body, and sometimes transmitted, sometimes reflected, when incident on a transparent medium of different density. To account for the particle being sometimes transmitted and sometimes reflected, Newton had recourse to the hypothesis of "fits of easy transmission and of easy reflection," and, to account for the fits themselves, he supposed the existence of an ether, the vibrations of which affected the particles. The laws of reflection were readily explained, being the same as for a perfectly elastic ball; the laws of refraction admitted of very simple explanation, by supposing that the particles of the denser medium exert a greater attraction on the particles of light than those of the rarer medium, but that this attraction acts only through very short distances, so that when the light-corpuscle is at a sensible distance from the surface, it is attracted equally all round, and moves as though there were no force acting upon it. As a consequence of this hypothesis, it follows that the velocity of light must be greater the denser the medium, while the undulatory theory leads to precisely the opposite result. When Foucault directly measured the velocity of light both in air and water, and found it less in the denser medium, the result was fatal to the corpuscular theory.

Dr. Young called attention to another crucial test between the two theories. When a piece of plate-glass is pressed against a slightly convex lens, or a watch-glass, a series of coloured rings is formed by reflected light, with a black spot in the centre. This was accounted for by Newton by supposing that the light which was reflected in any ring was in a fit of easy transmission (from glass to air) when it reached the first surface of the film of air, and in a fit of easy reflection when it reached the second surface. By measuring the thickness of a film of air corresponding to the first ring of any particular colour, the length of path corresponding to the interval between two fits for that particular kind of light could be determined. When water instead of air is placed between the glasses, according to the corpuscular theory the rings should expand; but according to the undulatory theory they should contract; for the wave-length corresponds to the distance between successive fits of the same kind on the corpuscular hypothesis. On trying the experiment, the rings were seen to contract. This result seemed to favour the undulatory theory; but the objection urged by Newton that rays of light do not bend round obstacles, like waves of sound, still held its ground. This objection Young completely demolished by his principle of interference. He showed that when light passes through an aperture in a screen, whatever the shape of the aperture, provided its width is large in comparison with the length of a wave of light (one fifty-thousandth of an inch), no sensible amount of light will reach any point not directly in front of the aperture; for if any point be taken to the right or left, the disturbances reaching that point from different points of the aperture will neutralize one another by interference, and thus no light will be appreciable. When the breadth of the aperture is only a small multiple of a wave-length, then there will be some points outside the direct beam at which the disturbances from different points of the aperture will not completely destroy one another, and others at which they will destroy one another; and these points will be different for light of different wave-lengths. In this way Young not only explained the rectilinear propagation of light, but accounted for the coloured bands formed when light diverges from a point through a very narrow aperture. In a similar way he accounted for the hyperbolic bands of colour observed by Grimaldi within the shadow of a square near its corners. With a strip of card one-thirtieth of an inch in width, Young obtained bands of colour within the shadow which completely disappeared when the light was cut off from either side of the strip of card, showing that they were produced by interference of the two portions of light which had passed, one to the right, the other to the left, of the strip of card. Professor Stokes has succeeded in showing a bright spot at the centre of the shadow of a circular disc of the size of a sovereign. The narrow bands of colour formed near the edge of the shadow of any object, which Newton supposed to be due to the "inflection" of the light by the attraction of the object, Young showed to be independent of the material or thickness of the edge, and completely accounted for them by the principle of interference. Newton's rings were explained with equal facility. They were due to the interference of light reflected from the first and second surfaces of the film of air or water between the glasses. The black spot at the centre of the reflected rings was due to the difference between reflection taking place from the surface of a denser or a rarer medium, half an undulation being lost when the reflection takes place in glass at the surface of air. If a little grease or water be placed between two pieces of glass which are nearly in contact, but the space between be not filled with the water or grease, but contain air in some parts, and water or grease in others, a series of rings will be seen by transmitted light, which have been called "the colours of mixed plates." Young showed that these colours could be accounted for by interference between the light that had passed through the air and that which had passed through the water, and explained the fact that, to obtain the same colour, the distance between the plates must be much greater than in the case of Newton's rings.

The bands of colour produced by the interference of light proceeding from a point and passing on each side of a narrow strip of card, have already been referred to. The bands are broader the narrower the strip of card. A fine hair gives very broad bands. When a number of hairs cross one another in all directions, these bands form circular rings of colour. If the width of the hairs be very variable, the rings formed will be of different sizes and overlapping one another, no distinct series will be visible; but when the hairs are of nearly the same diameter, a series of well-defined circles of colour, resembling Newton's rings, will be seen, and if the diameter of a particular ring be measured, the breadth of the hairs can be inferred. Young practically employed this method for measuring the diameter of the fibres of different qualities of wool in order to determine their commercial value. The instrument employed he called the *eriometer*. It consisted of a plate of brass pierced with a round hole about one-thirtieth of an inch in diameter in the centre, and around this a small circle, about one-third of an inch in diameter, of very fine holes. The plate was placed in front of a lamp, and the specimen of wool was held on wires at such a distance in front of the brass plate that the first green ring appeared to coincide with the circle of small holes. The eye was placed behind the lock of wool, and the distance to which the wool had to be removed in front of the brass plate in order that the first green ring might exactly coincide with the small circle of fine holes, was proportional to the breadth of the fibres. The same effect is produced if fine particles, such as lycopodium powder, or blood-corpuscles, scattered on a piece of glass, be substituted for the lock of wool, and Young employed the instrument in order to determine the diameter of blood-corpuscles. He determined the constant of his apparatus by comparison with some of Dr. Wollaston's micrometric observations. The coloured halos sometimes seen around the sun Young referred to the existence of small drops of water of nearly uniform diameter, and calculated the necessary diameter for halos of different angular magnitudes.

The same principle of interference afforded explanation of the colours of striated surfaces, such as mother-of-pearl, which vary with the direction in which they are seen. Viewed at one angle light of a particular colour reflected from different ridges will be in a condition to interfere, and this colour will be absent from the reflected light. At a different inclination, the light reaching the eye from all the ridges (within a certain angle) will be in precisely the same phase, and only then will light of that colour be reflected in its full intensity. With a micrometer scale engraved on glass by Coventry, and containing five hundred lines to the inch, Young obtained interference spectra. Modern gratings, with several thousand lines to the inch, afford the purest spectra that can be obtained, and enable the wave-length of any particular kind of light to be measured with the greatest accuracy.

Young's dislike of mathematical analysis prevented him from applying exact calculation to the interference phenomena which he observed, such as subsequently enabled Fresnel to overcome the prejudice of the French Academy and to establish the principle on an incontrovertible footing. Young's papers attracted very little attention, and Fresnel made for himself many of Young's earlier discoveries, but at once gave Young the full credit of the work when his priority was pointed out. The phenomena of polarization, however, still remained unexplained. Both Young and Fresnel had regarded the vibrations of light as similar to those of sound, and taking place in the direction in which the wave is propagated. The fact that light which had passed through a crystal of Iceland-spar, was differently affected by a second crystal, according to the direction of that crystal with respect to the former, showed that light which had been so transmitted was not like common light, symmetrical in all azimuths, but had acquired sides or poles. Such want of symmetry could not be accounted for on the hypothesis that the vibrations of light took place at right angles to the wave-front, that is, in the direction of propagation of the light. The polarization of light by reflection was discovered by Malus, in 1809. In a letter written to Arago, in 1817, Young hinted at the possibility of the existence of a component vibration at right angles to the direction of propagation, in light which had passed through Iceland-spar. In the following year Fresnel arrived independently at the hypothesis of transverse vibrations, not as constituting a small component of polarized light, but as representing completely the mode of vibration of all light, and in the hands of Fresnel this hypothesis of transverse vibrations led to a theory of polarization and double refraction both in uniaxal and biaxal crystals which, though it can hardly be regarded as complete from a mechanical point of view, is nevertheless one of the most beautiful and successful applications of mathematics to physics that has ever been made. To Young, however, belongs the credit of suggesting that the spheroidal form of the waves in Iceland-spar might be accounted for by supposing the elasticity different in the direction of the optic axis and at right angles to that direction; and he illustrated his view by reference to certain experiments of Chladni, in which it had been shown that the velocity of sound in the wood of the Scotch fir is different along, and perpendicular to, the fibre in the ratio of 5 to 4. Young was also the first to explain the colours exhibited by thin plates of crystals in polarized light, discovered by Arago in 1811, by the interference of the ordinary and extraordinary rays, and Fresnel afterwards completed Young's explanation in 1822.

It is for his contributions to the undulatory theory of light that Young will be most honourably remembered. Hooke, in 1664, referred to light as a "quick, short, vibrating motion;" Huyghens's "Traité de la Lumière" was published in 1690. From that time the undulatory theory lost ground, until it was revived by Young and Fresnel. It soon after received great support from the establishment, by Joule and others, of the mechanical theory of heat. One remark of Young's respecting the ether opens up a question which has attracted much attention of late years. In a letter addressed to the Secretary of the Royal Society, and read January 16, 1800, he says:—

> That a medium, resembling in many properties that which has been
> denominated ether, does really exist, is undeniably proved by the
> phenomena of electricity; and the arguments against the existence of
> such an ether throughout the universe have been pretty sufficiently
> answered by Euler. The rapid transmission of the electrical shock shows
> that the electric medium is possessed of an elasticity as great as is
> necessary to be supposed for the propagation of light. Whether the
> electric ether is to be considered as the same with the luminous ether—if
> such a fluid exists—may perhaps at some future time be discovered by
> experiment.

Besides his contributions to optics, Young made distinct advances in
connection with elasticity, and with surface-tension, or "capillarity." It is said
that Leonardo da Vinci was the first to notice the ascent of liquids in fine
tubes by so-called capillary attraction. This, however, is only one of a series
of phenomena now very generally recognized, and all of which are referable
to the same action. The hanging of a drop from the neck of a phial; the
pressure of air required to inflate a soap-bubble; the flotation of a greasy
needle on the surface of water; the manner in which some insects rest on
water, by depressing the surface, without wetting their legs; the possibility of
filling a tumbler with water until the surface stands above the edge of the
glass; the nearly spherical form of rain-drops and of small drops of mercury,
even when they are resting on a table,—are all examples of the effect of
surface-tension. These phenomena have recently been studied very carefully
by Quincke and Plateau, and they have been explained in accordance with the
principle of energy by Gauss. Hawksbee, however, was the first to notice that
the rise of a liquid in a fine tube did not depend on the thickness of the walls
of the tube, and he therefore inferred that, if the phenomena were due to the
attraction of the glass for the liquid, it could only be the superficial layers
which produced any effect. This was in 1709. Segner, in 1751, introduced the
notion of a surface-tension; and, according to his view, the surface of a liquid
must be considered as similar to a thin layer of stretched indiarubber, except
that the tension is always the same at the surface bounding the same media.
This idea of surface-tension was taken up by Young, who showed that it
afforded explanation of all the known phenomena of "capillarity," when
combined with the fact, which he was himself the first to observe, that the
angle of contact of the same liquid-surface with the same solid is constant.
This angle he called the "appropriate angle." But Young went further, and
attempted to explain the existence of surface-tension itself by supposing that
the particles of a liquid not only exert an attractive force on one another,

which is constant, but also a repulsive force which increases very rapidly when the distance between them is made very small. His views on this subject were embodied in a paper on the cohesion of liquids, read before the Royal Society in 1804. He afterwards wrote an article on the same subject for the supplement of the "Encyclopædia Britannica."

The changes which solids undergo under the action of external force, and their tendency to recover their natural forms, were studied by Hooke and Gravesande. The experimental fact that, for small changes of form, the extension of a rod or string is proportional to the tension to which it is exposed, is known as Hooke's law. The compression and extension of the fibres of a bent beam were noticed by James Bernoulli, in 1630, by Duhamel and others. The bending of beams was also studied by Coulomb and Robison, but Young appears to have been almost the first to apply the theory of elasticity to the statics of structures. In a letter to the Secretary of the Admiralty, written in 1811, in reply to an invitation to report on Mr. Steppings's improvements in naval architecture, Young claimed that he was the only person who had published "any attempts to improve the *theory* of carpentry." It may be here mentioned that Young accepted the invitation of the Admiralty, and sent in a very exhaustive report, which their Lordships regarded as "too learned" to be of great practical value. Young's contributions to this subject will be chiefly remembered in connection with his "modulus of elasticity." This he originally defined as follows:—

"The modulus of the elasticity of any substance is a column of the same substance capable of producing a pressure on its base which is to the weight causing a certain degree of compression as the length of the substance is to the diminution of its length."

It is not usual now to express Young's modulus of elasticity in terms of a length of the substance considered. As now usually defined, Young's modulus of elasticity is the force which would stretch a rod or string to double its natural length if Hooke's law were true for so great an extension.

So much of Dr. Young's scientific work has been mentioned here because it was during his early years of professional practice that his most original scientific work was accomplished. As already stated, after two years' tenure of the Natural Philosophy chair at the Royal Institution, Young resigned it because his friends were of opinion that its tenure militated against his prospects as a physician. In the summer of 1802 he escorted the great-nephews of the Duke of Richmond to Rouen, and took the opportunity of visiting Paris. In March, 1803, he took his degree of M.B. at Cambridge, and on June 14, 1804, he married Eliza, second daughter of J. P. Maxwell, Esq., whose country seat was near Farnborough. For sixteen years after his marriage, Young resided at Worthing during the summer, where he made a very respectable practice, returning to London in October or November. In January, 1811, he was elected one of the physicians of St. George's Hospital, which appointment he retained for the rest of his life. In this capacity his practice was considerably in advance of the times, for he regarded medicine as a science rather than an empirical art, and his careful methods of induction demanded an amount of attention which medical students, who preferred the more rough-and-ready methods then in vogue, were slow to give. The apothecary of the hospital stated that more of Dr. Young's patients went away cured than of those who were subjected to the more fashionable treatment; but his private practice, notwithstanding the sacrifices he had made, never became very valuable.

In 1816 Young was appointed Secretary to a Commission for determining the length of the second's pendulum. The reports of this Commission were drawn up by him, though the experimental work was carried out by Captain Kater. The result of the work was embodied in an Act of Parliament, introduced by Sir George Clerk, in 1824, which provided that if the standard yard should be lost it should "be restored to the same length," by making it bear to the length of the second's pendulum at sea-level in London, the ratio of 36 to 39·1393; but before the standards were destroyed, in 1835, so many sources of possible error were discovered in the reduction of pendulum observations, that the Commission appointed to restore the standards recommended that a material standard yard should be constructed, together with a number of copies, so that, in the event of the standard being again destroyed, it might be restored by comparison with its copies. In 1818 Young was appointed Superintendent of the Nautical Almanac and Secretary of the Board of Longitude. When this Board was dissolved in 1828, its functions were assumed by the Admiralty, and Young, Faraday, and Colonel Sabine were appointed a Scientific Committee of Reference to advise the Admiralty in all matters in which their assistance might be required. The income from these Government appointments rendered Young more independent of his practice, and he became less careful to publish his scientific papers anonymously. In 1820 he left Worthing and gave up his practice there. The following year, in company with Mrs. Young, he took a tour through France, Switzerland, and Italy, and at Paris attended a meeting of the Institute, where he met Arago, who had called on him in Worthing, in 1816. At the same time he made the acquaintance of Laplace, Cuvier, Humboldt, and others. In 1824 he visited Spa, and took a tour through Holland. In the same year Young was appointed Inspector of Calculations and Medical Referee to the Palladium Insurance Company. This caused him to turn his attention to the subject of life assurance and bills of mortality. In 1825, as Foreign Secretary of the Royal Society, he had the satisfaction of forwarding to Fresnel the Rumford Medal in acknowledgment of his researches on polarized light. Fresnel died, in his fortieth year, a few days after receiving the medal.

Dr. Young died on May 10, 1829, in the fifty-sixth year of his age, his excessive mental exertions in early life having apparently led to a premature old age. He was buried in the parish church of Farnborough, and a medallion by Sir Francis Chantrey was erected to his memory in Westminster Abbey.

But, though Young was essentially a scientific man, his accomplishments were all but universal, and any memoir of him would be very incomplete without some sketch of his researches in Egyptian hieroglyphics. His classical training, his extensive knowledge of European and Eastern languages, and his neat handwriting and drawing, have already been referred to. To these attainments must be added his scientific *method* and power of careful and systematic observation, and it will be seen that few persons could come to the task of deciphering an unknown language with a better chance of success than Dr. Young.

The Rosetta Stone was found by the French while excavating at Fort St. Pierre, near Rosetta, in 1799, and was brought to England in 1802. The stone bore an inscription in three different kinds of character—the Hieroglyphic, the Enchorial or Demotic, and the ordinary Greek. Young's attention was first called to the Egyptian characters by a manuscript which was submitted to him in 1814. He then obtained copies of the inscriptions on the Rosetta Stone and subjected them to a careful analysis. The latter part of the Greek inscription was very much injured, but was restored by the conjectures of Porson and Heyne, and read as follows:—"What is here decreed shall be inscribed on a block of hard stone, in sacred, in enchorial, and in Greek characters, and placed in each temple, of the first, second, and third gods."

This indicated that the three inscriptions contained the same decree, but, unfortunately, the beginnings of the first and second inscriptions were lost, so that there were no very definitely fixed points to start upon. The words "Alexander" and "Alexandria," however, occurred in the Greek, and these words, being so much alike, might be recognized in each of the other inscriptions. The word "Ptolemy" appeared eleven times in the Greek inscription, and there was a word which, from its length and position, seemed to correspond to it, which, however, appeared fourteen times in the hieroglyphic inscription. This word, whenever it appeared in the hieroglyphics, was surrounded by a ring forming what Champollion called a *cartouche*, which was always employed to denote the names of royal persons. These words were identified by Baron Sylvestre de Sacy and the Swedish scholar Akerblad. Young appears to have started with the idea, then generally current, that hieroglyphic symbols were purely ideographic, each sign representing a word. His knowledge of Chinese, however, led him to modify this view. In that language native words are represented by single symbols, but, when it is necessary to write a foreign word, a group of word-symbols is employed, each of which then assumes a phonetic character of the same value as the initial letter of the word which it represents. The phonetic value of these signs is indicated in Chinese by a line at the side, or by enclosing them in a square. Young supposed that the ring surrounding the royal names in the hieroglyphic inscription had the same value as the phonetic mark in Chinese, and from the symbols in the name of Ptolemy he commenced to construct a hieroglyphic alphabet. He made an error, however, in supposing that some of the symbols might be syllabic instead of alphabetic. It is true that in the older inscriptions single signs have sometimes a syllabic value, and sometimes are used ideographically, while in other cases a single sign representing the whole word is employed in conjunction with the alphabetic signs, probably to distinguish the word from others spelt in the same way, but in inscriptions of so late a date as the Rosetta Stone, the symbols were purely alphabetic. Another important step made by Young was the discovery of the use of *homophones*, or different symbols to represent the same letter. Young's work was closely followed up by Champollion, and afterwards by Lepsius, Birsch, and others. The greater part of his researches he never published, though he made careful examinations of several funeral rolls and other documents.

It would occupy too much space to give an adequate account of Young's researches in this subject; some portion of his work he published in a popular form in the article "Egypt," in the supplement of the "Encyclopædia Britannica," to which supplement he contributed about seventy articles on widely different subjects. Perhaps it is not too much to say that to Young we owe the foundation of all we now know of hieroglyphics and the Egyptian history which has been learned from them; and the obelisk on the Thames Embankment should call to mind the memory of no one more prominently than that of Thomas Young.

MICHAEL FARADAY.

The work of Michael Faraday introduced a new era in the history of physical science. Unencumbered by pre-existing theories, and untrammelled by the methods of the mathematician, he set forth on a line of his own, and, while engaged in the highest branches of experimental research, he sought to explain his results by reference to the most elementary mechanical principles only. Hence it was that those conclusions which had been obtained by mathematicians only by the help of advanced analytical methods, and which were expressed by them only in the language of the integral calculus, Faraday achieved without any such artificial aids to thought, and expressed in simple language, having reference to the mechanism which he conceived to be the means by which such results were brought about. For a long time Faraday's methods were regarded by mathematicians with something more than suspicion, and, while they could not but admire his experimental skill and were compelled to admit the accuracy of his conclusions, his mode of thought differed too widely from that to which they were accustomed to command their assent. In Sir William Thomson, and in Clerk Maxwell, Faraday at length found interpreters between him and the mathematical world, and to the mathematician perhaps the greatest monument of the genius of Faraday is the "Electricity and Magnetism" of Clerk Maxwell.

Michael Faraday was born at Newington, Surrey, on September 22, 1791, and was the third of four children. His father, James Faraday, was the son of Robert and Elizabeth Faraday, of Clapham Wood Hall, in the north-west of Yorkshire, and was brought up as a blacksmith. He was the third of ten children, and, in 1786, married Margaret Hastwell, a farmer's daughter. Soon after his marriage he came to London, where Michael was born. In 1796 James Faraday, with his family, moved from Newington, and took rooms over a coach-house in Jacob's Well Mews, Charles Street, Manchester Square. In looking at this humble abode one can scarcely help thinking that the Yorkshire blacksmith and his little family would have been far happier in a country "smiddy" near his native moors than in a crowded London court; but, had he remained there, it is difficult to see how the genius of young Michael could have met with the requisites for its development.

James Faraday was far from enjoying good health, and his illness often necessitated his absence from work, and, as a consequence, his family were frequently in very straitened circumstances. The early education of Michael was, therefore, not of a very high order, and consisted "of little more than the rudiments of reading, writing, and arithmetic." Like most boys in a similar position in London, he found his amusement for the most part in the streets, but, except that in his games at marbles we may assume that he played with other boys, we have no evidence whether his time was spent mostly by himself, or whether he was one of a "set" of street companions.

In 1804, when thirteen years of age, Michael Faraday went as errand-boy to Mr. Geo. Riebau, a bookseller in Blandford Street. Part of his duty in this capacity was to carry round papers lent on hire by his master, and in his "Life of Faraday," Dr. Bence Jones tells how anxious the young errand-boy was to collect his papers on Sunday morning in time to attend the Sandemanian service with the other members of his family.

Faraday was apprenticed to Mr. Riebau on October 7, 1805, and learned the business of a bookbinder. He occasionally occupied his spare time in reading the scientific books he had to bind, and was particularly interested in Mrs. Marcet's "Conversations in Chemistry," and in the article on "Electricity" in the "Encyclopædia Britannica." These were days before the existence of the London Society for the Extension of University Teaching, and, though Professor Anderson in Glasgow had shown how the advantages of a university might be extended to those whose fortunes prevented them from becoming regular university students, Professor Stuart had not yet taught the English universities that they had responsibilities outside their own borders, and that the national universities of the future must be the teachers of all classes of the community. But private enterprise supplied in a measure the neglect of public bodies. Mr. Tatum, of 43, Dorset Street, Fleet Street, advertised a course of lectures on natural philosophy, to be delivered at his residence at eight o'clock in the evenings. The price of admission was high, being a shilling for each lecture, but Michael's brother Robert frequently supplied him with the money, and in attending these lectures Faraday made many friendships which were valuable to him afterwards.

Faraday appears to have been aware of the value of skill in drawing—a point to which much attention has recently been called by those interested in technical education—and he spent some portion of his time in studying perspective, so as to be better able to illustrate his notes of Mr. Tatum's lectures, as well as of some of Sir Humphry Davy's, which he was enabled to hear at the Royal Institution through the kindness of a customer at Mr. Riebau's shop.

In 1812, before the end of his apprenticeship, Faraday was engaged in experiments with voltaic batteries of his own construction. Having cut out seven discs of zinc the size of halfpence, and covered them with seven halfpence, he formed a pile by inserting pieces of paper soaked in common salt between each pair, and found that the pile so constructed was capable of decomposing Epsom salts. With a somewhat larger pile he decomposed copper sulphate and lead acetate, and made some experiments on the decomposition of water. On July 21, 1812, in writing to his friend Abbott, he mentions the movements of camphor when floating on water, and adds, "Science may be illustrated by those minute actions and effects, almost as much as by more evident and obvious phenomena.... My knife is so bad that I cannot mend my pen with it; it is now covered with copper, having been employed to precipitate that metal from the muriatic acid."

Something of Faraday's disposition, as well as of the results of his self-education, may be gathered from the following quotations from letters to Abbott, written at this time:—

> I have again gone over your letter, but am so blinded that I cannot see any subject except chlorine to write on; but before entering on what I intend shall fill up the letter, I will ask your pardon for having maintained an opinion against one who was so ready to give his own up. I suspect from that circumstance I am wrong.... In the present case I conceive that experiments may be divided into three classes: first, those which are for the old theory of oxymuriatic acid, and consequently oppose the new one; second, those which are for the new one, and oppose the old theory; and third, those which can be explained by both theories—apparently so only, for in reality a false theory can never explain a fact."

> It is not for me to affirm that I am right and you wrong; speaking impartially, I can as well say that I am wrong and you right, or that we both are wrong and a third right. I am not so self-opinionated as to suppose that my judgment and perception in this or other matters is better or clearer than that of other persons; nor do I mean to affirm that this is the true theory in reality, but only that my judgment conceives it to be so. Judgments sometimes oppose each other, as in this case; and as there cannot be two opposing facts in nature, so there cannot be two opposing truths in the intellectual world. Consequently, when judgments oppose, one must be wrong—one must be false; and mine may be so for aught I can tell. I am not of a superior nature to estimate exactly the strength and correctness of my own and other men's understanding, and will assure you, dear A——, that I am far from being convinced that my own is always right. I have given you the theory—not as the true one, but as the one which appeared true to me—and when I perceive errors in it, I will immediately renounce it, in part or wholly, as my judgment may direct. From this, dear friend, you will see that I am very open to conviction; and from the manner in which I shall answer your letter, you

will also perceive that I must be convinced before I renounce.

On October 7, 1812, Faraday's apprenticeship terminated, and immediately afterwards he started life as a journeyman bookbinder. He now found that he had less time at his disposal for scientific work than he had enjoyed when an apprentice, and his desire to give up his trade and enter fully upon scientific pursuits became stronger than ever. During his apprenticeship he had written to Sir Joseph Banks, then President of the Royal Society, in the hope of obtaining some scientific employment; he now applied to Sir Humphry Davy. In a letter written to Dr. Paris, in 1829, Faraday gave an account of this application.

"My desire to escape from trade, which I thought vicious and selfish, and to enter into the service of science, which I imagined made its pursuers amiable and liberal, induced me at last to take the bold and simple step of writing to Sir H. Davy, expressing my wishes, and a hope that, if an opportunity came in his way, he would favour my views; at the same time, I sent the notes I had taken of his lectures.

"The answer, which makes all the point of my communication, I send you in the original, requesting you to take great care of it, and to let me have it back, for you may imagine how much I value it.

"You will observe that this took place at the end of the year 1812; and early in 1813 he requested to see me, and told me of the situation of assistant in the laboratory of the Royal Institution, then just vacant.

"At the same time that he thus gratified my desires as to scientific employment, he still advised me not to give up the prospects I had before me, telling me that Science was a harsh mistress, and, in a pecuniary point of view, but poorly rewarding those who devoted themselves to her service. He smiled at my notion of the superior moral feelings of philosophic men, and said he would leave me to the experience of a few years to set me right on that matter.

"Finally, through his good efforts, I went to the Royal Institution, early in March of 1813, as assistant in the laboratory; and in October of the same year went with him abroad, as his assistant in experiments and in writing. I returned with him in April, 1815, resumed my station in the Royal Institution, and have, as you know, ever since remained there."

Sir H. Davy's letter was as follows:—

"SIR,

"I am far from displeased with the proof you have given me of your

133

confidence, and which displays great zeal, power of memory, and attention. I am obliged to go out of town, and shall not be settled in town till the end of January; I will then see you at any time you wish. It would gratify me to be of any service to you; I wish it may be in my power.

"I am, sir,

Your obedient humble servant,

H. Davy.

The minutes of the meeting of managers of the Royal Institution, on March 1, 1813, contain the following entry:—"Sir Humphry Davy has the honour to inform the managers that he has found a person who is desirous to occupy the situation in the institution lately filled by William Payne. His name is Michael Faraday. He is a youth of twenty-two years of age. His habits seem good, his disposition active and cheerful, and his manner intelligent. He is willing to engage himself on the same terms as those given to Mr. Payne at the time of quitting the institution.

"Resolved, that Michael Faraday be engaged to fill the situation lately occupied by Mr. Payne, on the same terms."

About this time Faraday joined the City Philosophical Society, which had been started at Mr. Tatum's house in 1808. The members met every Wednesday evening, either for a lecture or discussion; and perhaps the society did not widely differ from some of the "students' associations" which have more recently been started in connection with other educational enterprises. Magrath was secretary of this society, and from it there sprang a smaller band of students, who, meeting once a week, either at Magrath's warehouse in Wood Street, or at Faraday's private rooms in the attics of the Royal Institution, for mutual improvement, read together, and freely criticized each other's pronunciation and composition. In a letter to Abbott six weeks after commencing work at the Royal Institution, Faraday says:—

A stranger would certainly think you and I were a couple of very simple beings, since we find it necessary to write to each other, though we so often personally meet; but the stranger would, in so judging, only fall into that error which envelops all those who decide from the outward appearances of things…. When writing to you I seek that opportunity of striving to describe a circumstance or an experiment clearly; so that you will see I am urged on by selfish motives partly to our mutual correspondence, but, though selfish, yet not censurable.

During the summer of 1813 Faraday, in his letters to Abbott, gave his friend the benefit of his experience "on the subject of lectures and lecturers in general," in a manner that speaks very highly of his power of observation of men as well as things. He was of opinion that a lecture should not last more than an hour, and that the subject should "fit the audience."

"A lecturer may consider his audience as being polite or vulgar (terms I wish you to understand according to Shuffleton's new dictionary), learned or unlearned (with respect to the subject), listeners or gazers. Polite company expect to be entertained, not only by the subject of the lecture, but by the manner of the lecturer; they look for respect, for language consonant to their dignity, and ideas on a level with their own. The vulgar—that is to say, in general, those who will take the trouble of thinking, and the bees of business —wish for something that they can comprehend. This may be deep and elaborate for the learned, but for those who are as yet tyros and unacquainted with the subject, must be simple and plain. Lastly, listeners expect reason and sense, whilst gazers only require a succession of words."

In favour of experimental illustration he says:—

"I need not point out ... the difference in the perceptive powers of the eye and the ear, and the facility and clearness with which the first of these organs conveys ideas to the mind—ideas which, being thus gained, are held far more retentively and firmly in the memory than when introduced by the ear.... Apparatus, therefore, is an essential part of every lecture in which it can be introduced.... When ... apparatus is to be exhibited, some kind of order should be observed in the arrangement of them on the lecture-table. Every particular part illustrative of the lecture should be in view, no one thing should hide another from the audience, nor should anything stand in the way of or obstruct the lecturer. They should be so placed, too, as to produce a kind of uniformity in appearance. No one part should appear naked and another crowded, unless some particular reason exists and makes it necessary to be so."

On October 13, 1813, Faraday left the Royal Institution, in order to accompany Sir Humphry Davy in a tour on the Continent. His journal gives some interesting details, showing the inconveniences of foreign travel at that time. Sir Humphry Davy took his carriage with him in pieces, and these had to be put together after escaping the dangers of the French custom-house on the quay at Morlaix, two years before the battle of Waterloo.

One apparently trivial incident somewhat marred Faraday's pleasure throughout this journey. It was originally intended that the party should comprise Sir Humphry and Lady Davy, Faraday, and Sir Humphry's valet, but at the last moment that most important functionary declined to leave his native shores. Davy then requested Faraday to undertake such of the duties of valet as were essential to the well-being of the party, promising to secure the services of a suitable person in Paris. But no eligible candidate appeared for the appointment, and thus Faraday had throughout to take charge of domestic affairs as well as to assist in experiments. Had there been only Sir Humphry and himself, this would have been no hardship. Sir Humphry had been accustomed to humble life in his early days; but the case was different with his lady, and, apparently, Faraday was more than once on the point of leaving his patron and returning home alone. A circumstance which occurred at Geneva illustrates the position of affairs. Professor E. de la Rive invited Sir Humphry and Lady Davy and Faraday to dinner. Sir Humphry could not go into society with one who, in some respects, acted as his valet. When this point was represented to the professor, he replied that he was sorry, as it would necessitate his giving another dinner-party. Faraday subsequently kept up a correspondence with De la Rive, and continued it with his son. In writing to the latter he says, in speaking of Professor E. de la Rive, that he was "the first who personally at Geneva, and afterwards by correspondence, encouraged and by that sustained me."

At Paris Faraday met many of the most distinguished men of science of the time. One morning Ampère, Clément, and Desormes called on Davy, to show him some iodine, a substance which had been discovered only about two years before, and Davy, while in Paris, and afterwards at Montpellier, executed a series of experiments upon it. After three months' stay, the party left Paris for Italy, *viâ* Montpellier, Aix, and Nice, whence they crossed the Col de Tende to Turin. The transfer of the carriage and baggage across the Alps was effected by a party of sixty-five men, with sledges and a number of mules. The description of the journey, as recorded in Faraday's diary, makes us respect the courage of an Englishman who, in the early part of this century, would attempt the conveyance of a carriage across the Alps in the winter.

"From Turin we proceeded to Genoa, which place we left afterwards in an open boat, and proceeded by sea towards Lerici. This place we reached after a very disagreeable passage, and not without apprehensions of being overset by the way. As there was nothing there very enticing, we continued our route to Florence; and, after a stay of three weeks or a month, left that fine city, and in four days arrived here at Rome." The foregoing is from Faraday's letter to his mother. At Florence a good deal of time was spent in the Academia del Cimento. Here Faraday saw the telescope with which Galileo discovered Jupiter's satellites, with its tube of wood and paper about three feet and a half long, and simple object-glass and eye-glass. A red velvet electric machine with a rubber of gold paper, Leyden jars pierced by the discharge between their armatures, the first lens constructed by Galileo, and a number of other objects, were full of interest to the recently enfranchised bookbinder's apprentice; but it was the great burning-glass of the grand-duke which was the most serviceable of all the treasures of the museum. With this glass—which consisted of two convex lenses about three feet six inches apart, the first lens having a diameter of about fourteen or fifteen inches, and the second a diameter of three inches—Davy succeeded in burning several diamonds in oxygen gas, and in proving that the diamond consists of little else than carbon. In 1818 Faraday published a paper on this subject in the *Quarterly Journal of Science*. At Genoa some experiments were made with the torpedo, but the specimens caught were very small and weak, and their shocks so feeble that no definite results were obtained. At Rome Davy attempted to repeat an experiment of Signor Morrichini, whereby a steel needle was magnetized by causing the concentrated violet and blue rays from the sun to traverse the needle from the middle to the north end several times. The experiment did not succeed in the hands of Davy and Faraday, and it was left to the latter to discover a relation between magnetism and light. From Rome they visited Naples and ascended Vesuvius, and shortly afterwards left Italy for Geneva. In the autumn of 1814 they returned from Switzerland through Germany, visiting Berne, Zurich, the Tyrol, Padua, Venice, and Bologne, to Florence, where Davy again carried out some chemical investigations in the laboratory of the academy. Thence they returned to Rome, and in the spring went on to Naples, and again visited Vesuvius, returning to England in April, *viâ* Rome, the Tyrol, Stuttgart, Brussels, and Ostend.

A fortnight after his return from the Continent Faraday was again assistant at the Royal Institution, but with a salary of thirty shillings a week. His character will be sufficiently evident from the quotations which have been given from his diary and letters. Henceforth we must be mainly occupied with the consideration of his scientific work.

In January, 1816, he gave his first lecture to the City Philosophical Society. In a lecture delivered shortly afterwards before the same society, the following passage, which gives an idea of one of the current beliefs of the time, occurs:
—

"The conclusion that is now generally received appears to be that light consists of minute atoms of matter of an octahedral form, possessing polarity, and varying in size or in velocity....

"If now we conceive a change as far beyond vaporization as that is above fluidity, and then take into account also the proportional increased extent of alteration as the changes rise, we shall, perhaps, if we can form any conception at all, not fall far short of radiant matter;[6] and as in the last conversion many qualities were lost, so here also many more would disappear.

"It was the opinion of Newton, and of many other distinguished philosophers, that this conversion was possible, and continually going on in the processes of nature, and they found that the idea would bear without injury the application of mathematical reasoning—as regards heat, for instance. If assumed, we must also assume the simplicity of matter; for it would follow that all the variety of substances with which we are acquainted could be converted into one of three kinds of radiant matter, which again may differ from one another only in the size of their particles or their form. The properties of known bodies would then be supposed to arise from the varied arrangements of their ultimate atoms, and belong to substances only as long as their compound nature existed; and thus variety of matter and variety of properties would be found co-essential. The simplicity of such a system is singularly beautiful, the idea grand and worthy of Newton's approbation. It was what the ancients believed, and it may be what a future race will realize."

In the closing words of his fifth lecture to the City Philosophical Society, Faraday said:—

"The philosopher should be a man willing to listen to every suggestion, but determined to judge for himself. He should not be biassed by any appearances; have no favourite hypothesis; be of no school; and in doctrine have no master. He should not be a respecter of persons, but of things. Truth should be his primary object. If to these qualities be added industry, he may indeed hope to walk within the veil of the temple of nature."

Many years afterwards he stated that, of all the suggestions to which he had patiently listened after his lectures at the Royal Institution, only one proved on investigation to be of any value, and that led to the discovery of the "extra current" and the whole subject of self-induction.

Faraday always kept a note-book, in which he jotted down any thoughts which occurred to him in reference to his work, as well as extracts from books or other publications which attracted his attention. He called it his "commonplace-book." Many of the queries which he here took note of he subsequently answered by experiment. For example:—

"Query: the nature of sounds produced by flame in tubes."

"Convert magnetism into electricity."

"General effects of compression, either in condensing gases or producing solutions, or even giving combinations at low temperature."

"Do the pith-balls diverge by the disturbance of electricity through mutual induction or not?"

Speaking of this book, he says, "I already owe much to these notes, and think such a collection worth the making by every scientific man. I am sure none would think the trouble lost after a year's experience."

In a letter dated May 3, 1818, he writes:—

I have this evening been busy with an atmospherical electrical apparatus. It was a very temporary thing, but answered the purpose completely. A wire, with some small brush-wire rolled round the top of it, was elevated into the atmosphere by a thin wood rod having a glass tube at the end, and tied to a chimney-pot on the housetop; and this wire was continued down (taking care that it touched nothing in its way) into the lecture-room; and we succeeded, at intervals, in getting sparks from it nearly a quarter of an inch in length, and in charging a Leyden jar, so as to give a strong shock. The electricity was positive. Now, I think you could easily make an apparatus of this kind, and it would be a constant source of interesting matter; only take care you do not kill yourself or knock down the house.

On June 12, 1820, he married Miss Sarah Barnard, third daughter of Mr. Barnard, of Paternoster Row—"an event which," to use his own words, "more than any other contributed to his earthly happiness and healthful state of mind." It was his wish that the day should be "just like any other day"—that there should be "no bustle, no noise, no hurry occasioned even in one day's proceeding," though in carrying out this plan he offended some of his relations by not inviting them to his wedding.

Up to this time Faraday's experimental researches had been for the most part in the domain of chemistry, and for two years a great part of his energy had been expended in investigating, in company with Mr. Stodart, a surgical instrument-maker, the properties of certain alloys of steel, with a view to improve its manufacture for special purposes. It was in 1821 that he commenced his great discoveries in electricity. In the autumn of that year he wrote an historical sketch of electro-magnetism for the "Annals of Philosophy," and he repeated for himself most of the experiments which he described. In the course of these experiments, in September, 1821, he discovered the rotation of a wire conveying an electric current around the pole of a magnet. Œrsted had discovered, in 1820, the tendency of a magnetic needle to set itself at right angles to a wire conveying a current. This action is due to a tendency on the part of the north pole to revolve in a right-handed direction around the current, while the south pole tends to revolve in the opposite direction. The principle that action and reaction are equal and opposite indicates that, if a magnetic pole tend to rotate around a conductor conveying a current, there must be an equal tendency for the conductor to rotate around the pole. It was this rotation that constituted Faraday's first great discovery in electro-dynamics. On December 21, in the same year, Faraday showed that the earth's magnetism was capable of exerting a directive action on a wire conveying a current. Writing to De la Rive on the subject, he says: —

I find all the usual attractions and repulsions of the magnetic needle by the conjunctive wire are deceptions, the motions being, not attractions or repulsions, nor the result of any attractive or repulsive forces, but the result of a force in the wire, which, instead of bringing the pole of the needle nearer to or further from the wire, endeavours to make it move round it in a never-ending circle and motion whilst the battery remains in action. I have succeeded, not only in showing the existence of this motion theoretically, but experimentally, and have been able to make the wire revolve round a magnetic pole, or a magnetic pole round the wire, at pleasure. The law of revolution, and to which all the other motions of the needle are reducible, is simple and beautiful.

Conceive a portion of connecting wire north and south, the north end being attached to the positive pole of a battery, the south to the negative. A north magnetic pole would then pass round it continually in the apparent direction of the sun, from east to west above, and from west to east below. Reverse the connections with the battery, and the motion of the pole is reversed; or, if the south pole be made to revolve, the motions will be in the opposite direction, as with the north pole.

If the wire be made to revolve round the pole, the motions are according to those mentioned.... Now, I have been able, experimentally, to trace this motion into its various forms, as exhibited by Ampère's helices, etc., and in all cases to show that the attractions and repulsions are only appearances due to this circulation of the pole; to show that dissimilar poles repel as well as attract, and that similar poles attract as well as repel; and to make, I think, the analogy between the helix and common bar magnet far stronger than before. But yet I am by no means decided that there are currents of electricity in the common magnet. I have no doubt that electricity puts the circles of the helix into the same state as those circles are in that may be conceived in the bar magnet; but I am not certain that this state is directly dependent on the electricity, or that it cannot be produced by other agencies; and therefore, until the presence of electric currents be proved in the magnet by other than magnetical effects, I shall remain in doubt about Ampère's theory.

The most convenient rule by which to remember the direction of these electro-magnetic rotations is probably that given by Clerk Maxwell, which will be stated in its place.[7] If a circular plate of copper and another of zinc be connected by a piece (or better, by three pieces) of insulated wire, so that the zinc is about an inch above the copper, and the combined plates be suspended by a silk fibre in a small beaker of dilute sulphuric acid, which is placed on the pole of a large magnet, the liquid will be seen to rotate about a vertical axis in one direction, and the two plates with their connecting wires in the opposite direction. On reversing the polarity of the magnet, both rotations will be reversed. This is a very simple mode of exhibiting Faraday's discovery. A little powdered resin renders the motion of the liquid readily visible.

[7] See p. 302.

In 1823 Faraday published his work on the liquefaction of gases, from which he concluded that there was no difference in kind between gases and vapours. In the course of this work he met with more than one serious explosion. On January 8, 1824, he was elected a Fellow of the Royal Society, and in 1825, on the recommendation of Sir Humphry Davy, he was appointed Director of the Laboratory of the Royal Institution, and in this capacity he instituted the laboratory conferences, which developed into the Friday evening lectures. For five years after this, the greater part of Faraday's spare time was occupied in some investigations in connection with optical glass, made at the request of the Royal Society, and at the expense of the Government. Mr. Dollond and Sir John Herschel were associated with him on this committee, but the results obtained were not of much value to opticians. The silico-borate of lead which Faraday prepared in the course of these experiments was, however, the substance with which he first demonstrated the effect of a magnetic field on the plane of polarization of light, and with which he discovered diamagnetic action.

Faraday's experimental researches were generally guided by theoretical considerations. Frequently these theories were based on very slender premises, and sometimes were little else than flights of a scientific imagination, but they served to guide him into fruitful fields of discovery, and he seldom placed much confidence in his conclusions till he had succeeded in verifying them experimentally. For many years he had held the opinion that electric currents should exhibit phenomena analogous to those of electro-static induction. Again and again he returned to the investigation, and attempted to obtain an induced current in one wire through the passage of a powerful current through a neighbouring conductor; but he looked for a permanent induced current to be maintained during the whole time that the primary current was flowing. At length, employing two wires wound together as a helix on a wooden rod, the first capable of transmitting a powerful current from a battery, while the second was connected with a galvanometer, he observed that, when the current started in the primary, there was a movement of the galvanometer, and when it ceased there was a movement in the opposite direction, though the galvanometer remained at zero while the current continued steady. Hence it was apparent that it is by changes in the primary current that induced currents may be generated, and not by their steady continuance; and it was demonstrated that, when a current is started in a conductor, a temporary current is induced in a neighbouring conductor in the opposite direction, while a current is induced in the same direction as the primary when the latter ceases to flow. Before obtaining this result with the wires on a wooden bobbin, he had experimented with a wrought-iron ring about six inches in diameter, and made of 7/8-inch round iron. He wound two sets of coils round it, one occupying nearly half the ring, and the other filling most of the other half. One of these he connected with a galvanometer, the other could be connected at will with a battery. On sending the battery current through the latter coil, the galvanometer needle swung completely round four or five times, and a similar action took place, but in the opposite direction, on stopping the current. Here it was clearly the magnetism induced in the iron ring which produced so powerful a current in the galvanometer circuit. Next he wound a quantity of covered copper wire on a small iron bar, and connecting the ends to a galvanometer, he placed the little bobbin between the opposite poles of a pair of bar magnets, whose other ends were in contact. As soon as the iron core touched the magnets, a current appeared in the galvanometer. On breaking contact, the current was in the opposite direction. Then came the experiment above mentioned, in which no iron was employed. After this, one end of a cylindrical bar magnet was introduced into a helix of copper wire, and then suddenly thrust completely in. The galvanometer connected with the coil showed a transient current. On withdrawing the magnet, the current appeared in the opposite direction; so that currents were induced merely by the relative motion of a magnet and a conductor.

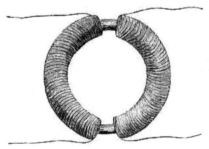

A copper disc was mounted so that it could be made to rotate rapidly. A wire was placed in connection with the centre of the disc, and the circuit completed by a rubbing contact on the circumference. A galvanometer was inserted in the circuit, and the large horseshoe magnet of the Royal Institution so placed that the portion of the disc between the centre and the rubbing contact passed between the poles of the magnet. A current flowed through the galvanometer as long as the disc was kept spinning. Then he found that the mere passage of a copper wire between the poles of the magnet was sufficient to induce a current in it, and concluded that the production of the current was connected with the cutting of the "magnetic curves," or "lines of magnetic force" which would be depicted by iron filings. Thus in the course of ten days' experimental work, in the autumn of 1831, Faraday so completely investigated the phenomena of electro-magnetic induction as to leave little, except practical applications, to his successors. A few weeks later he obtained induction currents by means of the earth's magnetism only, first with a coil of wire wound upon an iron bar in which a strong current was produced when it was being quickly placed in the direction of the magnetic dip or being removed from that position, and afterwards with a coil of wire without an iron core. On February 8, 1832, he succeeded in obtaining a spark from the induced current. Unless the electro-motive force is very great, it is not possible to obtain a spark between two metallic surfaces which are separated by a sensible thickness of air. If, however, the circuit of a wire is broken *while* the current is passing, a little bridge of metallic vapour is formed, across which for an instant the spark leaps. The induced current being of such short duration, the difficulty was to break the circuit while it was flowing. Faraday wound a considerable length of fine wire around a short bar of iron; the ends of the wire were crossed so as just to be in contact with one another, but free to separate if exposed to a slight shock. The ends of the iron bar projected beyond the coil, and were held just over the poles of the magnet. On releasing the bar it fell so as to strike the magnetic poles and close the circuit of the magnet. An induced current was generated in the wire, but, while this was passing, the shock caused by the bar striking the magnet separated the ends of the wire, thus breaking the circuit of the conductor, and a spark appeared at the gap. In this little spark was the germ of the electric light of to-day. Subsequently Faraday improved the apparatus, by attaching a little disc of amalgamated copper to one end of the wire, and bending over the other end so as just to press lightly against the surface of the disc. With this apparatus he showed the "magnetic spark" at the meeting of the British Association at Oxford.

Faraday supposed that when a coil of wire was in the neighbourhood of a magnet, or near to a conductor conveying a current, the coil was thrown into a peculiar condition, which he called the *electro-tonic state*, and that the induced currents appeared whenever this state was assumed or lost by the coil. He frequently reverted to his conception of the electro-tonic state, though he saw clearly that, when the currents were induced by the relative motion of a wire and a magnet, the current induced depended on the rate at which the lines of magnetic force had been cut by the wire. Of his conception of lines of force filling the whole of space, we shall have more to say presently. It is sufficient to remark here that, in the electro-tonic state of Faraday, Clerk Maxwell recognized the number of lines of magnetic force enclosed by the circuit, and showed that the electro-motive force induced is proportional to the rate of change of the number of lines of force thus enclosed.

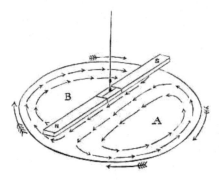

It is seldom that a great discovery is made which has not been gradually led up to by several observed phenomena which awaited that discovery for their explanation. In the case of electro-magnetic induction, however, there appears to have been but one experiment which had baffled philosophers, and the key to which was found in Faraday's discovery, while the complete explanation was given by Faraday himself. Arago had found that, if a copper plate were made rapidly to rotate beneath a freely suspended magnetic needle, the needle followed (slowly) the plate in its revolution, though a sheet of glass were inserted between the two to prevent any air-currents acting on the magnet. The experiment had been repeated by Sir John Herschel and Mr. Babbage, but no explanation was forthcoming. Faraday saw that the revolution of the disc beneath the poles of the magnet must generate induced currents in the disc, as the different portions of the metal would be constantly cutting the lines of force of the magnet. These currents would react upon the magnet, causing a mechanical stress to act between the two, which, as stated by Lenz, would be in the direction tending to oppose the *relative* motion, and therefore to drag the magnet after the disc in its revolution. In the above figure the unfledged arrows show the general distribution of the currents in the disc, while the winged arrows indicate the direction of the disc's rotation. The currents in the semicircle A will repel the north pole and attract the south pole. Those in the semicircle B will produce the opposite effect, and hence there will be a

144

tendency for the magnet to revolve in the direction of the disc, while the motion of the disc will be resisted. This resistance to the motion of a conductor in a magnetic field was noticed by Faraday, and, independently, by Tyndall, and it is sufficiently obvious in the power absorbed by dynamos when they are generating large currents.

Faraday's next series of researches was devoted to the experimental proof of the identity of frictional and voltaic electricity. He showed that a magnet could be deflected and iodide of potassium decomposed by the current from his electrical machine, and came to the conclusion that the amount of electricity required to decompose a grain of water was equal to 800,000 charges of his large Leyden battery. The current from the frictional machine also served to deflect the needle of his galvanometer. These investigations led on to a complete series of researches on the laws of electrolysis, wherein Faraday demonstrated the principle that, however the strength of the current may be varied, the amount of any compound decomposed is proportional to the whole quantity of electricity which has passed through the electrolyte. When the same current is sent through different compounds, there is a constant relation between the amounts of the several compounds decomposed. In modern language, Faraday's laws may be thus expressed:—

If the same current be made to pass through several different electrolytes, the quantity of each ion produced will be proportional to its combining weight divided by its valency, and if the current vary, the quantity of each ion liberated per second will be proportional to the current.

This is the great law of electro-chemical equivalents. The amount of hydrogen liberated per second by a current of one ampère is about ·00001038 gramme, or nearly one six-thousandth of a grain. This is the electro-chemical equivalent of hydrogen. That of any other substance may be found by Faraday's law.

From Faraday's results it appears that the passage of the same amount of electricity is required in order to decompose one molecule of any compound of the same chemical type, but it does not follow that the same amount of energy is employed in the decomposition. For example, the combining weights of copper and zinc are nearly equal. Hence it will require the passage of about the same amount of electricity to liberate a pound of copper from, say, the copper sulphate as to liberate a pound of zinc from zinc sulphate; but the work to be done is much less in the case of the copper. This is made manifest in the following way:—A battery, which will just decompose the copper salt slowly, liberating copper, oxygen, and sulphuric acid, will not decompose the zinc salt at all so as to liberate metallic zinc, but immediately on sending the current through the electrolyte, polarization will set in, and the opposing electro-motive force thus introduced will become equal to that of the battery, and stop the current before metallic zinc makes its appearance. In the case of the copper, polarization also sets in, but never attains to equality with the electro-motive force of the primary battery. In fact, in all cases of electrolysis, polarization produces an opposing electro-motive force strictly proportional to the work done in the cell by the passage of each unit of electricity. If the strength of the battery be increased, so that it is able to decompose the zinc sulphate, and if this battery be applied to the copper sulphate solution, the latter will be *rapidly* decomposed, and the excess of energy developed by the battery will be converted into heat in the circuit.

One important point in connection with electrolysis which Faraday demonstrated is that the decomposition is the result of the passage of the current, and is not simply due to the attraction of the electrodes. Thus he showed that potassium iodide could be decomposed by a stream of electricity coming from a metallic point on the prime conductor of his electric machine, though the point did not touch the test-paper on which the iodide was placed.

It was in 1834 that Mr. Wm. Jenkin, after one of the Friday evening lectures at the Royal Institution, called the attention of Faraday to a shock which he had experienced in breaking the circuit of an electro-magnet, though the battery employed consisted of only one pair of plates. Faraday repeated the experiment, and found that, with a large magnet in circuit, a strong spark could thus be obtained. On November 14, 1834, he writes, "The phenomenon of increased spark is merely a case of the induction of electric currents. If a current be established in a wire, and another wire forming a complete circuit be placed parallel to it, at the moment the current in the first is stopped it induces a current in the same direction in the second, itself then showing but a feeble spark. But if the second be away, it induces a current in its own wire in the same direction, producing a strong spark. The strong spark in the current when alone is therefore the equivalent of the current it can produce in a neighbouring wire when in company." The strong spark does, in fact, represent the energy of the current due to the self-induction of its circuit, which energy would, in part at least, be expended in inducing a current in a neighbouring wire if such existed.

His time from 1835 till 1838 was largely taken up with his work on electro-static induction. Faraday could never be content with any explanation based on direct action at a distance; he always sought for the machinery through which the action was communicated. In this search the lines of magnetic force, which he had so often delineated in iron filings, came to his aid. Faraday made many pictures in iron filings of magnetic fields due to various combinations of magnets. He employed gummed paper, and when the filings were arranged on the hard gummed surface, he projected a feeble jet of steam on the paper, which melted the gum and fixed the filings. Several of his diagrams were exhibited at the Loan Collection at South Kensington. He conceived electrical action to be transmitted along such lines as these, and to him the whole electric field was filled with lines passing always from positive to negative electrification, and in some respects resembling elastic strings. The action at any place could then be expressed in terms of the lines of force that existed there, the electrifications by which these lines were produced being left out of consideration. The acting bodies were thus replaced by the field of force they produced. He showed that it was impossible to call into existence a charge of positive electricity without at the same time producing an equal negative charge. From every unit of positive electricity he conceived a line of force to start, and thus, with the origin of the line, there was created simultaneously a charge of negative electricity on which the line might terminate. By the famous ice-pail experiment he showed that, when a charged body is inserted in a closed or nearly closed hollow conductor, an equal amount of the same kind of electricity appeared on the outside of the hollow conductor, while an equal amount of the opposite kind appeared on the interior surface of the conductor. With the ice-pail and the butterfly-net he showed that there could be no free electricity on the interior of a conductor. Lines of force cannot pass through the material of a conductor without producing electric displacement. Every element of electricity must be joined to an equal amount of the opposite kind by a line of force. Such lines cannot pass through the conductor itself; hence the charge must be entirely on the outside of the conductor, so that every element of the charge may be associated with an equal amount of the opposite electricity upon the surfaces of surrounding objects. Thus to Faraday every electrical action was an exhibition of electric induction. All this work had been done before by Henry Cavendish, but neither Faraday nor any one else knew about it at the time. From the fact that there could be no electricity in the interior of a hollow conductor, Cavendish deduced, in the best way possible, the truth of the law of inverse squares as applied to electrical attraction and repulsion, and thus laid the foundation of the mathematical theory of electricity. To Cavendish every electrical action was a displacement of an incompressible fluid which filled the whole of space, producing no effect in conductors on account of the freedom of its motion, but producing strains in insulators by displacing the material of the body. Faraday, in his lines of force, saw, as it were, the lines along which the displacements of Cavendish's fluid took place.

Faraday thought that, if he could show that electric induction could take place along curved lines, it would prove that the action took place through a medium, and not directly at a distance. He succeeded in experimentally demonstrating the curvature of these lines; but his conclusions were not warranted, for if we conceive of two or more centres of force acting directly at a distance according to the law of inverse squares, the resultant lines of force will generally be curved. Of course, this does not prove the possibility of direct action at a distance, but only shows that the curvature of the lines is as much a consequence of the one hypothesis as of the other.

It soon appeared to Faraday that the nature of the dielectric had very much to do with electric induction. The capacity of a condenser, for instance, depends on the nature of the dielectric as well as on the configuration of the conductors. To express this property, Faraday employed the term "specific inductive capacity." He compared the electric capacity of condensers, equal in all other respects, but one possessing air for its dielectric, and the other having other media, and thus roughly determined the specific inductive capacities of several insulators. These results turned out afterwards to be of great value in connection with the insulation of submarine cables. Even now the student of electricity is sometimes puzzled by the manner in which specific inductive capacity is introduced to his notice as modifying the capacity of condensers, after learning that the capacity of any system of conductors can be calculated from its geometrical configuration; but the fact is that the intensity of all electrical actions depends on the nature of the medium through which they take place, and it will require more electricity to exert upon an equal charge a unit force at unit distance when the intervening medium has a high than when it possesses a low specific inductive capacity.

In 1835 Faraday received a pension from the civil list; in 1836 he was appointed scientific adviser to the Elder Brethren of the Trinity House. In the same year he was made a member of the Senate of the University of London, and in that capacity he has exerted no small influence on the scientific education of the country, for he was one of those who drew up the schedules of the various examinations.

In his early years, Faraday thought that all kinds of matter might ultimately consist of three materials only, and that as gases and vapours appeared more nearly to resemble one another than the liquids or solids to which they corresponded, so each might be subject to a still higher change in the same direction, and the gas or vapour become radiant matter—either heat, light, or electricity. Later on, Faraday clearly recognized the dynamical nature of heat and light; but his work was always guided by his theoretical conceptions of the "correlation of the physical forces." For a long time he had tried to discover relations between electricity and light; at length, on September 13, 1845, after experimenting on a number of other substances, he placed a piece of silico-borate of lead, or heavy-glass, in the field of the magnet, and found that, when a beam of polarized light was transmitted through the glass in the direction of the lines of magnetic force, there was a rotation of the plane of polarization. Afterwards it appeared that all the transparent solids and liquids experimented on were capable of producing this rotation in a greater or less degree, and in the case of all non-magnetic substances the rotation was in the direction of the electric current, which, passing round the substance, would produce the magnetic field employed. Abandoning the magnet, and using only a coil of wire with the transparent substance within it, similar effects were obtained. Thus at length a relation was found between light and electricity.

On November 4, employing a piece of heavy-glass and a new horseshoe magnet, Faraday noticed that the magnet appeared to have a directive action upon the glass. Further examination showed that the glass was repelled by the magnetic poles. Three days afterwards he found that all sorts of substances, including most metals, were acted upon like the heavy-glass. Small portions of them were repelled, while elongated cylinders tended to set with their lengths perpendicular to the lines of magnetic force. Such actions could be imitated by suspending a feebly magnetic body in a medium more magnetic than itself. Faraday, therefore, sought for some medium which would be absolutely neutral to magnetic action. Filling a glass tube with compressed oxygen, and suspending it in an atmosphere of oxygen at ordinary pressure, the compressed gas behaved like iron or other magnetic substances. Faraday compared the intensity of its action with that of ferrous sulphate, and this led to an explanation of the diurnal variations of the compass-needle based on the sun's heat diminishing the magnetic *permeability* of the oxygen of the air. Repeating the experiment with nitrogen, he found that the compressed gas behaved in a perfectly neutral manner when surrounded by the gas at ordinary pressure. Hence he inferred that in nitrogen he had found the neutral medium required. Repeating his experiments in an atmosphere of nitrogen, it still appeared that most bodies were repelled by the magnetic poles, and set *equatorially*, or at right angles to the lines of force when elongated portions were tested. To this action Faraday gave the name of diamagnetism.

About a month after his marriage, Faraday joined the Sandemanian Church, to which his family had for several generations belonged, by confession of sin and profession of faith. Not unfrequently he used to speak at the meetings of his Church, but in 1840 he was elected an elder, and then he took his turn regularly in conducting the services. The notes of his addresses he generally made on small pieces of card. He had a curious habit of separating his religious belief from his scientific work, although the spirit of his religion perpetually pervaded his life. A lecture on mental education, given in 1854, at the Royal Institution, in the presence of the late Prince Consort, he commenced as follows:—

"Before entering on this subject, I must make one distinction, which, however it may appear to others, is to me of the utmost importance. High as man is placed above the creatures around him, there is a higher and far more exalted position within his view; and the ways are infinite in which he occupies his thoughts about the fears, or hopes, or expectations of a future life. I believe that the truth of that future cannot be brought to his knowledge by any exertion of his mental powers, however exalted they may be; that it is made known to him by other teaching than his own, and is received through simple belief of the testimony given. Let no one suppose for a moment that the self-education I am about to commend, in respect of the things of this life, extends to any considerations of the hope set before us, as if man by reasoning could find out God. It would be improper here to enter upon this subject further than to claim an absolute distinction between religious and ordinary belief. I shall be reproached with the weakness of refusing to apply those mental operations which I think good in respect of high things to the very highest. I am content to bear the reproach. Yet even in earthly matters I believe that 'the invisible things of Him from the creation of the world are clearly seen, being understood by the things that are made, even His eternal power and Godhead;' and I have never seen anything incompatible between those things of man which can be known by the spirit of man which is within him, and those higher things concerning his future which he cannot know by that spirit."

On more than one occasion the late Prince Consort had discussed physical questions with Faraday, and in 1858 the Queen offered him a house on Hampton Court Green. This was his home until August 25, 1867. He saw not only the magnetic spark, which he had first produced, employed in the lighthouses at the South Foreland and Dungeness, but he saw also his views respecting lines of electric induction examined and confirmed by the investigations of Thomson and Clerk Maxwell.

Of the ninety-five distinctions conferred upon him, we need only mention that of Commandant of the Legion of Honour, which he received in January, 1856.

JAMES CLERK MAXWELL.

The story of the life of James Clerk Maxwell has been told so recently by the able pen of his lifelong friend, Professor Lewis Campbell, that it is unnecessary, in the few pages which now remain to us, to attempt to give a repetition of the tale which would not only fail to do justice to its subject, but must of necessity fall far short of the merits of the (confessedly imperfect) sketch which has recently been placed within the reach of all. Looking back on the life of Clerk Maxwell, he seems to have come amongst us as a light from another world—to have but partly revealed his message to minds too often incapable of grasping its full meaning, and all too soon to have returned to the source from whence he came. There was scarcely any branch of natural philosophy that he did not grapple with, and upon which his vivid imagination and far-seeing intelligence did not throw light. He was born a philosopher, and at every step Nature partly drew aside the veil and revealed that which was hidden from a gaze less prophetic. A very brief sketch of the principal incidents in his life may, however, not be out of place.

James Clerk Maxwell was born in Edinburgh, on June 13, 1831. His father, John Clerk Maxwell, was the second son of James Clerk, of Penicuik, and took the name of Maxwell on inheriting the estate at Middlesbie. His mother was the daughter of R. H. Cay, Esq., of North Charlton, Northumberland. James was the only child who survived infancy.

Some years before his birth his parents had built a house at Glenlair, which had been added to their Middlesbie estate, and resided there during the greater part of the year, though they retained their house in Edinburgh. Hence it was that James's boyish days were spent almost entirely in the country, until he entered the Edinburgh Academy in 1841. As a child, he was never content until he had completely investigated everything which attracted his attention, such as the hidden courses of bell-wires, water-streams, and the like. His constant question was "What's the go o' that?" and, if answered in terms too general for his satisfaction, he would continue, "But what's the particular go of it?" This desire for the thorough investigation of every phenomenon was a characteristic of his mind through life. From a child his knowledge of Scripture was extensive and accurate, and when eight years old he could repeat the whole of the hundred and nineteenth psalm. About this time his mother died, and thenceforward he and his father became constant companions. Together they would devise all sorts of ingenious mechanical contrivances. Young James was essentially a child of nature, and free from all conventionality. He loved every living thing, and took delight in petting young frogs, and putting them into his mouth to see them jump out. One of his attainments was to paddle on the duck-pond in a wash-tub, and to make the vessel go "without spinning"—a recreation which had to be relinquished on washing-days. He was never without the companionship of one or two terriers, to whom he taught many tricks, and with whom he seemed to have complete sympathy.

As a boy, Maxwell was not one to profit much by the ordinary teaching of the schools, and experience with a private tutor at home did not lead to very satisfactory results. At the age of ten, therefore, he was sent to the Edinburgh Academy, under the care of Archdeacon Williams, who was then rector. On his first appearance in this fashionable school, he was naturally a source of amusement to his companions; but he held his ground, and soon gained more respect than he had previously provoked ridicule. While at school in Edinburgh, he resided with his father's sister, Mrs. Wedderburn, and devoted a very considerable share of his time and attention to relieving the solitude of the old man at Glenlair, by letters written in quaint styles, sometimes backwards, sometimes in cypher, sometimes in different colours, so arranged that the characters written in a particular colour, when placed consecutively, formed another sentence. All the details of his school and home life, and the special peculiarities of the masters at the academy, were thus faithfully transmitted to his father, by whom the letters were religiously preserved. At thirteen he had evidently made progress in solid geometry, though he had not commenced Euclid, for he writes to his father, "I have made a tetrahedron, a dodecahedron, and two other hedrons whose names I don't know." In these letters to Glenlair he generally signed himself, "Your most obedient servant." Sometimes his fun found vent even upon the envelope; for example:—

Mr. John Clerk Maxwell,

"Postyknowswere,

"Kirkpatrick Durham,

"Dumfries."

Sometimes he would seal his letters with electrotypes of natural objects (beetles, etc.), of his own making. In July, 1845, he writes:—

I have got the eleventh prize for scholarship, the first for English, the prize for English verses, and the mathematical medal.

When only fifteen a paper on oval curves was contributed by him to the *Proceedings of the Royal Society of Edinburgh*. In the spring of 1847 he accompanied his uncle on a visit to Mr. Nicol, the inventor of the Nicol prism, and on his return he made a polariscope with glass and a lucifer-match box, and sketched in water-colours the chromatic appearances presented by pieces of unannealed glass which he himself prepared. These sketches he sent to Mr. Nicol, who presented him in return with a pair of prisms of his own construction. The prisms are now in the Cavendish Laboratory at Cambridge. Maxwell found that, for unannealed glass, pieces of window-glass placed in bundles of eight or nine, one on the other, answered the purpose very well. He cut the figures, triangles, squares, etc., with a diamond, heated the pieces of glass on an iron plate to redness in the kitchen fire, and then dropped them into a plate of iron sparks (scales from the smithy) to cool.

In 1847 Maxwell entered the University of Edinburgh, and during his course of study there he contributed to the Royal Society of Edinburgh papers upon rolling curves and on the equilibrium of elastic solids. His attention was mostly devoted to mathematics, physics, chemistry, and mental and moral philosophy. In 1850 he went to Cambridge, entering Peterhouse, but at the end of a year he "migrated" to Trinity; here he was soon surrounded with a circle of friends who helped to render his Cambridge life a very happy one. His love of experiment sometimes extended to his own mode of life, and once he tried sleeping in the evening and working after midnight, but this was soon given up at the request of his father. One of his friends writes, "From 2 to 2.30 a.m. he took exercise by running along the upper corridor, *down* the stairs, along the lower corridor, then *up* the stairs, and so on until the inhabitants of the rooms along his track got up and laid *perdus* behind their sporting-doors, to have shots at him with boots, hair-brushes, etc., as he passed." His love of fun, his sharp wit, his extensive knowledge, and above all, his complete unselfishness, rendered him a universal favourite in spite of the temporary inconveniences which his experiments may have occasionally caused to his fellow-students.

An undergraduate friend writes, "Every one who knew him at Trinity can recall some kindness or some act of his which has left an ineffaceable impression of his goodness on the memory—for 'good' Maxwell was in the best sense of the word." The same friend wrote in his diary in 1854, after meeting Maxwell at a social gathering, "Maxwell, as usual, showing himself acquainted with every subject on which the conversation turned. I never met a man like him. I do believe there is not a single subject on which he cannot talk, and talk well too, displaying always the most curious and out-of-the-way information." His private tutor, the late well-known Mr. Hopkins, said of him, "It is not possible for that man to think incorrectly on physical subjects."

In 1854 Maxwell took his degree at Cambridge as second wrangler, and was

bracketed with the senior wrangler (Mr. E. J. Routh) for the Smith's prize. During his undergraduate course, he appears to have done much of the work which formed the basis of his subsequent papers on electricity, particularly that on Faraday's lines of force. The colour-top and colour-box appear also to have been gradually developing during this time, while the principle of the stereoscope and the "art of squinting" received their due share of attention. Shortly after his degree, he devoted a considerable amount of time to the preparation of a manuscript on geometrical optics, which was intended to form a university text-book, but was never completed. In the autumn of 1855 he was elected Fellow of Trinity. About this time the colour-top was in full swing, and he also constructed an ophthalmoscope. In May, 1855, he writes:
—

> The colour trick came off on Monday, 7th. I had the proof-sheets of my paper, and was going to read; but I changed my mind and talked instead, which was more to the purpose. There were sundry men who thought that blue and yellow make green, so I had to undeceive them. I have got Hay's book of colours out of the University Library, and am working through the specimens, matching them with the top.

The "colour trick" came off before the Cambridge Philosophical Society.

While a Bachelor Fellow, Maxwell gave lectures to working men in Barnwell, besides lecturing in college. His father died in April, 1856, and shortly afterwards he was appointed Professor of Natural Philosophy in Marischal College, Aberdeen. This appointment he held until the fusion of the college with King's College in 1860. These four years were very productive of valuable work. During them the dynamical top was constructed, which illustrates the motion of a rigid body about its axis of greatest, least, or mean moment of inertia; for, by the movement of certain screws, the axis of the top may be made to coincide with any one at will. The Adams Prize Essay on the stability of Saturn's rings belongs also to this period. In this essay Maxwell showed that the phenomena presented by Saturn's rings can only be explained on the supposition that they consist of innumerable small bodies—"a flight of brickbats"—each independent of all the others, and revolving round Saturn as a satellite. He compared them to a siege of Sebastopol from a battery of guns measuring thirty thousand miles in one direction, and a hundred miles in the other, the shots never stopping, but revolving round a circle of a hundred and seventy thousand miles radius. A solid ring of such dimensions would be completely crushed by its own weight, though made of the strongest material of which we have any knowledge. If revolving at such a rate as to balance the attraction of the planet at one part, the stress in other parts would be more than sufficient to crush or tear the ring. Laplace had shown that a narrow ring might revolve about the planet and be stable if so loaded that its centre of gravity was at a considerable distance from its centre, and thought that Saturn's rings might consist of a number of such unsymmetrical rings—a theory to which some support was given by the many small divisions observable in the bright rings. Maxwell showed that, for stability, the mass required to load each of Laplace's rings must be four and a half times that of the rest of the ring; and the system would then be far too artificially balanced to be proof against the action of one ring on another. He further showed that, in liquid rings, waves would be produced by the mutual action of the rings, and that before long some of these waves would be sure to acquire such an amplitude as would cause the rings to break up into small portions. Finally, he concluded that the only admissible theory is that of the independent satellites, and that the *average* density of the rings so found cannot be much greater than that of air at ordinary pressure and temperature.

While he remained at Aberdeen, Maxwell lectured to working men in the evenings, on the principles of mechanics. On the whole, it is doubtful whether Aberdeen society was as congenial to him as that of Cambridge or Edinburgh. He seems not to have been understood even by his colleagues. On one occasion he wrote:—

> Gaiety is just beginning here again.... No jokes of any kind are understood here. I have not made one for two months, and if I feel one coming I shall bite my tongue.

But every cloud has its bright side, and, however Maxwell may have been regarded by his colleagues, he was not long without congenial companionships. An honoured guest at the home of the Principal, "in February, 1858, he announced his betrothal to Katherine Mary Dewar, and they were married early in the following June." Professor Campbell speaks of his married life as one of unexampled devotion, and those who enjoyed the great privilege of seeing him at home could more than endorse the description.

In 1860 Maxwell accepted the chair of Natural Philosophy at King's College, London. Here he continued his lectures to working men, and even kept them up for one session after resigning the chair in 1865. On May 17, 1861, he gave his first lecture at the Royal Institution, on "The Theory of the Three Primary Colours." This lecture embodies many of the results of his work with the colour-top and colour-box, to be again referred to presently. While at King's College, he was placed on the Electrical Standards Committee of the British Association, and most of the work of the committee was carried out in his laboratory. Here, too, he compared the electro-static repulsion between two discs of brass with the electro-magnetic attraction of two coils of wire surrounding them, through which a current of electricity was allowed to flow, and obtained a result which he afterwards applied to the electro-magnetic theory of light. The colour-box was perfected, and his experiments on the viscosity of gases were concluded during his residence in London. These last were described by him in the Bakerian Lecture for 1866.

After resigning the professorship at King's College, Maxwell spent most of his time at Glenlair, having enlarged the house, in accordance with his father's original plans. Here he completed his great work on "Electricity and Magnetism," as well as his "Theory of Heat," an elementary text-book which may be said to be without a parallel.

On March 8, 1871, he accepted the chair of Experimental Physics in the University of Cambridge. This chair was founded in consequence of an offer made by the Duke of Devonshire, the Chancellor of the University, to build and equip a physical laboratory for the use of the university. In this capacity Maxwell's first duty was to prepare plans for the laboratory. With this view, he inspected the laboratories of Sir William Thomson at Glasgow, and of Professor Clifton at Oxford, and endeavoured to embody the best points of both in the new building. The result was that, in conjunction with Mr. W. M. Fawcett, the architect, he secured for the university a laboratory noble in its exterior, and admirably adapted to the purposes for which it is required. The ground-floor comprises a large battery-room, which is also used as a storeroom for chemicals; a workshop; a room for receiving goods, communicating by a lift with the apparatus-room; a room for experiments on heat; balance-rooms; a room for pendulum experiments, and other investigations requiring great stability; and a magnetic observatory. The last two rooms are furnished with stone supports for instruments, erected on foundations independent of those of the building, and preserved from contact with the floor. On the first floor is a handsome lecture-theatre, capable of accommodating nearly two hundred students. The lecture-table is carried on a wall, which passes up through the floor without touching it, the joists being borne by separate brick piers. The lecture-theatre occupies the height of the first and second floors; its ceiling is of wood, the panels of which can be removed, thus affording access to the roof-principals, from which a load of half a ton or more may be safely suspended over the lecture-table. The panels of the ceiling, adjoining the wall which is behind the lecturer, can also be readily removed, and a "window" in this wall communicates with the large electrical-room on the second floor. Access to the space above the ceiling of the lecture-theatre is readily obtained from the tower. Adjoining the lecture-room is the preparation-room, and communicating with the latter is the apparatus-room. This room is fitted with mahogany and plate-glass wall and central cases, and at present contains, besides the more valuable portions of the apparatus belonging to the laboratory, the marble bust of James Clerk Maxwell, and many of the home-made pieces of apparatus and other relics of his early work. The rest of the first floor is occupied by the professor's private room and the general students' laboratory. Throughout the building the brick walls have been left bare for convenience in attaching slats or shelves for the support of instruments. The second floor contains a large room for electrical experiments, a dark room for photography, and a number of private rooms for original work. Water is laid on to every room, including a small room in the top of the tower, and all the windows are provided with broad stone ledges without and within the window, the two portions being in the same horizontal plane, for the support of heliostats or other instruments. The building is heated with hot water, but in the magnetic observatory the pipes are all of copper and the fittings of gun-metal. Open fireplaces for basket fires are also provided. Over the principal entrance of the laboratory is placed a stone statue of the present Duke of Devonshire, together with the arms of the university and of the Cavendish family, and the Cavendish motto, "Cavendo Tutus." Maxwell presented to the laboratory, in 1874, all the apparatus in his possession. He usually gave a course of lectures on heat and the constitution of bodies in the Michaelmas term; on electricity in the Lent term; and on electro-magnetism in the Easter term. The following extract from his inaugural lecture, delivered in October, 1871, is worthy of the attention of all students of science:—

Science appears to us with a very different aspect after we have found out that it is not in lecture-rooms only, and by means of the electric light projected on a screen, that we may witness physical phenomena, but that we may find illustrations of the highest doctrines of science in games and gymnastics, in travelling by land and by water, in storms of the air and of the sea, and wherever there is matter in motion.

The habit of recognizing principles amid the endless variety of their action can never degrade our sense of the sublimity of nature, or mar our enjoyment of its beauty. On the contrary, it tends to rescue our scientific ideas from that vague condition in which we too often leave them, buried among the other products of a lazy credulity, and to raise them into their proper position among the doctrines in which our faith is so assured that we are ready at all times to act on them. Experiments of illustration may be of very different kinds. Some may be adaptations of the commonest operations of ordinary life; others may be carefully arranged exhibitions of some phenomenon which occurs only under peculiar conditions. They all, however, agree in this, that their aim is to present some phenomenon to the senses of the student in such a way that he may associate with it some appropriate scientific idea. When he has grasped this idea, the experiment which illustrates it has served its purpose.

In an experiment of research, on the other hand, this is not the principal aim.... Experiments of this class—those in which measurement of some kind is involved—are the proper work of a physical laboratory. In every experiment we have first to make our senses familiar with the phenomenon; but we must not stop here—we must find out which of its features are capable of measurement, and what measurements are required in order to make a complete specification of the phenomenon. We must then make these measurements, and deduce from them the result which we require to find.

This characteristic of modern experiments—that they consist principally of measurements—is so prominent that the opinion seems to have got abroad that, in a few years, all the great physical constants will have been approximately estimated, and that the only occupation which will then be left to men of science will be to carry these measurements to another place of decimals.

If this is really the state of things to which we are approaching, our laboratory may, perhaps, become celebrated as a place of conscientious labour and consummate skill; but it will be out of place in the university, and ought rather to be classed with the other great workshops of our country, where equal ability is directed to more useful ends.

But we have no right to think thus of the unsearchable riches of creation, or of the untried fertility of those fresh minds into which these riches will continually be poured.... The history of Science shows that, even during that phase of her progress in which she devotes herself to improving the accuracy of the numerical measurement of quantities with which she has long been familiar, she is preparing the materials for the subjugation of new regions, which would have remained unknown if she had been contented with the rough methods of her early pioneers.

Maxwell's "Electricity and Magnetism" was published in 1873. Shortly afterwards there were placed in his hands, by the Duke of Devonshire, the Cavendish Manuscripts on Electricity, already alluded to. To these he devoted much of his spare time for several years, and many of Cavendish's experiments were repeated in the laboratory by Maxwell himself, or under his direction by his students. The introductory matter and notes embodied in "The Electrical Researches of the Honourable Henry Cavendish, F.R.S.," afford sufficient evidence of the amount of labour he expended over this work. The volume was published only a few weeks before his death. Another of Maxwell's publications, which, as a text-book, is unique and beyond praise, is the little book on "Matter and Motion," published by the S.P.C.K.

In 1878 Maxwell, at the request of the Vice-Chancellor, delivered the Rede Lecture in the Senate-House. His subject was the telephone, which was just then absorbing a considerable amount of public attention. This was the last lecture which he ever gave to a large public audience.

It was during his tenure of the Cambridge chair that one of the cottages on the Glenlair estate was struck by lightning. The discharge passed down the damp soot and blew out several stones from the base of the chimney, apparently making its way to some water in a ditch a few yards distant. The cottage was built on a granite rock, and this event set Maxwell thinking about the best way to protect, from lightning, buildings which are erected on granite or other non-conducting foundations. He decided that the proper course was to place a strip of metal upon the ground all round the building, to carry another strip along the ridge-stay, from which one or more pointed rods should project upwards, and to unite this strip with that upon the ground by copper strips passing down each corner of the building, which is thus, as it were, enclosed in a metal cage.

After a brief illness, Maxwell passed away on November 5, 1879. His intellect and memory remained perfect to the last, and his love of fun scarcely diminished. During his illness he would frequently repeat hymns, especially some of George Herbert's, and Richard Baxter's hymn beginning

> "Lord, it belongs not to my care."

"No man ever met his death more consciously or more calmly."

It has been stated that Thomas Young propounded a theory of colour-vision which assumes that there exist three separate colour-sensations, corresponding to red, green, and violet, each having its own special organs, the excitement of which causes the perception of the corresponding colour, other colours being due to the excitement of two or more of these simple sensations in different proportions. Maxwell adopted blue instead of violet for the third sensation, and showed that if a particular red, green, and blue were selected and placed at the angular points of an equilateral triangle, the colours formed by mixing them being arranged as in Young's diagram, all the shades of the spectrum would be ranged along the sides of this triangle, the centre being neutral grey. For the mixing of coloured lights, he at first employed the colour-top, but, instead of painting circles with coloured sectors, the angles of which could not be changed, he used circular discs of coloured paper slit along one radius. Any number of such discs can be combined so that each shows a sector at the top, and the angle of each sector can be varied at will by sliding the corresponding disc between the others. Maxwell used discs of two different sizes, the small discs being placed above the larger on the same pivot, so that one set formed a central circle, and the other set a ring surrounding it. He found that, with discs of five different colours, of which one might be white and another black, it was always possible to combine them so that the inner circle and the outer ring exactly matched. From this he showed that there could be only three conditions to be satisfied in the eye, for two conditions were necessitated by the nature of the top, since the smaller sectors must exactly fill the circle and so must the larger. Maxwell's experiments, therefore, confirmed, in general, Young's theory. They showed, however, that the relative delicacy of the several colour-sensations is different in different eyes, for the arrangement which produced an exact match in the case of one observer, had to be modified for another; but this difference of delicacy proved to be very conspicuous in colour-blind persons, for in most of the cases of colour-blindness examined by Maxwell the red sensation was completely absent, so that only two conditions were required by colour-blind eyes, and a match could therefore always be made in such cases with four discs only. Holmgren has since discovered cases of colour-blindness in which the violet sensation is absent. He agrees with Young in making the third sensation correspond to violet rather than blue. Maxwell explained the fact that persons colour-blind to the red divide colours into blues and yellows by the consideration that, although yellow is a complex sensation corresponding to a mixture of red and green, yet in nature yellow tints are so much brighter than greens that they excite the green sensation more than green objects themselves can do, and hence greens and yellows are called yellow by such colour-blind persons, though their perception of yellow is really the same as perception of green by normal eyes. Later on, by a combination of adjustable slits, prisms, and lenses arranged in a "colour-box," Maxwell succeeded in mixing, in any desired proportions, the light from any three portions of the spectrum, so that he could deal with pure spectral colours instead of the complex combinations of differently coloured lights afforded by coloured papers. From these experiments it appears that no ray of the solar spectrum can affect one colour-sensation alone, so that there are no colours in nature so pure as to correspond to the pure simple sensations, and the colours occupying the angular points of Maxwell's diagram affect all three colour-sensations, though they influence two of them to a much smaller extent than the third. A particular colour in the spectrum corresponds to light which, according to the undulatory theory, physically consists of waves all of the same period, but it may affect all three of the colour-sensations of a normal eye, though in different proportions. Thus, yellow light of a given wave-length affects the red and green sensations considerably and the blue (or violet) slightly, and the same effect may be produced by various mixtures of red or orange and green. For his researches on the perception of colour, the Royal Society awarded to Clerk Maxwell the Rumford Medal in 1860.

Another optical contrivance of Maxwell's was a wheel of life, in which the usual slits were replaced by concave lenses of such focal length that the picture on the opposite side of the cylinder appeared, when seen through a lens, at the centre, and thus remained apparently fixed in position while the cylinder revolved. The same result has since been secured by a different contrivance in the praxinoscope.

Another ingenious optical apparatus was a real-image stereoscope, in which two lenses were placed side by side at a distance apart equal to half the distance between the pictures on the stereoscopic slide. These lenses were placed in front of the pictures at a distance equal to twice their focal length. The real images of the two pictures were then superposed in front of the lenses at the same distance from them as the pictures, and these combined images were looked at through a large convex lens.

The great difference in the sensibility to different colours of the eyes of dark and fair persons when the light fell upon the *fovea centralis*, led Maxwell to the discovery of the extreme want of sensibility of this portion of the retina to blue light. This he made manifest by looking through a bottle containing solution of chrome alum, when the central portion of the field of view appears of a light red colour for the first second or two.

A more important discovery was that of double refraction temporarily produced in viscous liquids. Maxwell found that a quantity of Canada balsam, if stirred, acquired double-refracting powers, which it retained for a short period, until the stress temporarily induced had disappeared.

But Maxwell's investigations in optics must be regarded as his play; his real work lay in the domains of electricity and of molecular physics.

In 1738 Daniel Bernouilli published an explanation of atmospheric pressure on the hypothesis that air consists of a number of minute particles moving in all directions, and impinging on any surface exposed to their action. In 1847 Herapath explained the diffusion of gases on the hypothesis that they consisted of perfectly hard molecules impinging on one another and on surfaces exposed to them, and pointed out the relation between their motion and the temperature and pressure of a gas. The present condition of the molecular theory of gases, and of molecular science generally, is due almost entirely to the work of Joule, Clausius, Boltzmann, and Maxwell. To Maxwell is due the general method of solving all problems connected with vast numbers of individuals—a method which he called the statistical method, and which consists, in the first place, in separating the individuals into groups, each fulfilling a particular condition, but paying no attention to the history of any individual, which may pass from one group to another in any way and as often as it pleases without attracting attention. Maxwell was the first to estimate the average distance through which a particle of gas passes without coming into collision with another particle. He found that, in the case of hydrogen, at standard pressure and temperature, it is about 1/250000 of an inch; for air, about 1/389000 of an inch. These results he deduced from his experiments on viscosity, and he gave a complete explanation of the viscosity of gases, showing it to be due to the "diffusion of momentum" accompanying the diffusion of material particles between the passing streams of gas.

One portion of the theory of electricity had been considerably developed by Cavendish; the application of mathematics to the theory of attractions, and hence to that of electricity, had been carried to a great degree of perfection by Laplace, Lagrange, Poisson, Green, and others. Faraday, however, could not satisfy himself with a mathematical theory based upon direct action at a distance, and he filled space, as we have seen, with tubes of force passing from one body to another whenever there existed any electrical action between them. These conceptions of Faraday were regarded with suspicion by mathematicians. Sir William Thomson was the first to look upon them with favour; and in 1846 he showed that electro-static force might be treated mathematically in the same way as the flow of heat; so that there are, at any rate, two methods by which the fundamental formulæ of electro-statics can be deduced. But it is to Maxwell that mathematicians are indebted for a complete exposition of Faraday's views in their own language, and this was given in a paper wherein the phenomena of electro-statics were deduced as results of a stress in a medium which, as suggested by Newton and believed by Faraday, might well be that same medium which serves for the propagation of light; and "the lines of force" were shown to correspond to an actual condition of the medium when under electrical stress. Maxwell, in fact, showed, not only that Faraday's lines formed a consistent system which would bear the most stringent mathematical analysis, but were more than a conventional system, and might correspond to a state of stress actually existing in the medium through which they passed, and that a tension along these lines, accompanied by an equal pressure in every direction at right angles to them, would be consistent with the equilibrium of the medium, and explain, on mechanical principles, the observed phenomena. The greater part of this work he accomplished while an undergraduate at Cambridge. He showed, too, that Faraday's conceptions were equally applicable to the case of electro-magnetism, and that all the laws of the induction of currents might be concisely expressed in Faraday's language. Defining the positive direction through a circuit in which a current flows as the direction in which a right-handed screw would advance if rotating with the current, and the positive direction around a wire conveying a current as the direction in which a right-handed screw would rotate if advancing with the current, Maxwell pointed out that the lines of magnetic force due to an electric current always pass round it, or through its circuit, in the positive direction, and that, *whenever the number of lines of magnetic force passing through a closed circuit is changed, there is an electro-motive force round the circuit represented by the rate of diminution of the number of lines of force which pass through the circuit in the positive direction.*

The words in italics form a complete statement of the laws regulating the production of currents by the motion of magnets or of other currents, or by the variation of other currents in the neighbourhood. Maxwell showed, too, that Faraday's electro-tonic state, on the variation of which induced currents depend, corresponds completely with the number of lines of magnetic force passing through the circuit.

He also showed that, when a conductor conveying a current is free to move in a magnetic field, or magnets are free to move in the neighbourhood of such a conductor, *the system will assume that condition in which the greatest possible number of lines of magnetic force pass through the circuit in the positive direction.*

But Maxwell was not content with showing that Faraday's conceptions were consistent, and had their mathematical equivalents,—he proceeded to point out how a medium could be imagined so constituted as to be able to perform all the various duties which were thus thrown upon it. Assuming a medium to be made up of spherical, or nearly spherical, cells, and that, when magnetic force is transmitted, these cells are made to rotate about diameters coinciding in direction with the lines of force, the tension along those lines, and the pressure at right angles to them, are accounted for by the tendency of a rotating elastic sphere to contract along its polar axis and expand equatorially so as to form an oblate spheroid. By supposing minute spherical particles to exist between the rotating cells, the motion of one may be transmitted in the same direction to the next, and these particles may be supposed to constitute electricity, and roll as perfectly rough bodies on the cells in contact with them. Maxwell further imagined the rotating cells, and therefore, *à fortiori*, the electrical particles, to be extremely small compared with molecules of matter; and that, in conductors, the electrical particles could pass from molecule to molecule, though opposed by friction, but that in insulators no such transference was possible. The machinery was then complete. If the electric particles were made to flow in a conductor in one direction, passing between the cells, or *molecular vortices*, they compelled them to rotate, and the rotation was communicated from cell to cell in expanding circles by the electric particles, acting as idle wheels, between them. Thus rings of magnetic force were made to surround the current, and to continue as long as the current lasted. If an attempt were made to displace the electric particles in a dielectric, they would move only within the substance of each molecule, and not from molecule to molecule, and thus the cells would be deformed, though no continuous motion would result. The deformation of the cells would involve elastic stress in the medium. Again, if a stream of electric particles were started into motion, and if there were another stream of particles in the neighbourhood free to flow, though resisted by friction, these particles, instead of at once transmitting the rotary motion of the cells on one side of them to the cells on the other side, would at first, on account of the inertia of the cells, begin to move themselves with a motion of translation opposite to that of the primary current, and the motion would only gradually be destroyed by the frictional resistance and the molecular vortices on the other side made to revolve with their full velocity. A similar effect, but in the opposite direction, would take place if the primary current ceased, the vortices not stopping all at once if there were any possibility of their continuing in motion. The imaginary medium thus serves for the production of induced currents.

The mechanical forces between currents and magnets and between currents and currents, as well as between magnets and currents, were accounted for by the tension and pressure produced by the molecular vortices. When currents are flowing in the same direction in neighbouring conductors, the vortices in the space between them are urged in opposite directions by the two currents, and remain almost at rest; the lateral pressure exerted by those on the outside of the conductors is thus unbalanced, and the conductors are pushed together as though they attracted each other. When the currents flow in opposite directions in parallel conductors, they conspire to give a greater velocity to the vortices in the space between them, than to those outside them, and are thus pushed apart by the pressure due to the rotation of the vortices, as though they repelled each other. In a similar way, the actions of magnets on conductors conveying currents may be explained. The motion of a conductor across a series of lines of magnetic force may squeeze together and lengthen the threads of vortices in front, and thus increase their speed of rotation, while the vortices behind will move more slowly because allowed to contract axially and expand transversely. The velocity of the vortices thus being greater on one side of the wire than the other, a current must be induced in the wire. Thus the current induced by the motion of a conductor in a magnetic field may be accounted for.

This conception of a medium was given by Maxwell, not as a theory, but to show that it was possible to devise a *mechanism* capable, in imagination at least, of producing all the phenomena of electricity and magnetism. "According to our theory, the particles which form the partitions between the cells constitute the matter of electricity. The motion of these particles constitutes an electric current; the tangential force with which the particles are pressed by the matter of the cells is electro-motive force; and the pressure of the particles on each other corresponds to the tension or potential of the electricity."

When a current is maintained in a wire, the molecular vortices in the surrounding space are kept in uniform motion; but if an attempt be made to stop the current, since this would necessitate the stoppage of the vortices, it is clear that it cannot take place suddenly, but the energy of the vortices must be in some way used up. For the same reason it is impossible for a current to be suddenly started by a finite force. Thus the phenomena of self-induction are accounted for by the supposed medium.

The magnetic permeability of a medium Maxwell identified with the density of the substance composing the rotating cells, and the specific inductive capacity he showed to be inversely proportional to its elasticity. He then proved that the ratio of the electro-magnetic unit to the electro-static unit must be equal to the velocity of transmission of a transverse vibration in the medium, and consequently proportional to the square root of the elasticity, and inversely proportional to the square root of the density. If the medium is the same as that engaged in the propagation of light, then this ratio ought to be equal to the velocity of light, and, moreover, in non-magnetic media, the refractive index should be proportional to the square root of the specific inductive capacity. The different measurements which had been made of the ratio of the electrical units gave a mean very nearly coinciding with the best determinations of the velocity of light, and thus the truth underlying Maxwell's speculation was strikingly confirmed, for the velocity of light was determined by purely electrical measurements. In the case also of bodies whose chemical structure was not very complicated, the refractive index was found to agree fairly well with the square root of the specific inductive capacity; but the phenomenon of "residual charge" rendered the accurate measurement of the latter quantity a matter of great difficulty. It therefore appeared highly probable that light is an electro-magnetic disturbance due to a motion of the electric particles in an insulating medium producing a strain in the medium, which becomes propagated from particle to particle to an indefinite distance. In the case of a conductor, the electric particles so displaced would pass from molecule to molecule against a frictional resistance, and thus dissipate the energy of the disturbance, so that true (*i.e.* metallic) conductors must be nearly impervious to light; and this also agrees with experience.

Maxwell thus furnished a complete theory of electrical and electro-magnetic action in which all the effects are due to actions propagated in a medium, and direct action at a distance is dispensed with, and exposed his theory successfully to most severe tests. In his great work on electricity and magnetism, he gives the mathematical theory of all the above actions, without, however, committing himself to any particular form of mechanism to represent the constitution of the medium. "This part of that book," Professor Tait says, "is one of the most splendid monuments ever raised by the genius of a single individual.... There seems to be no longer any possibility of doubt that Maxwell has taken the first grand step towards the discovery of the true nature of electrical phenomena. Had he done nothing but this, his fame would have been secured for all time. But, striking as it is, this forms only one small part of the contents of this marvellous work."

CONCLUSION.

SOME OF THE RESULTS OF FARADAY'S DISCOVERIES, AND THE
PRINCIPLE OF ENERGY.

In early days, *the spirit of the amber*, when aroused by rubbing, came forth
and took to itself such light objects as it could easily lift. Later on, and the
spirit gave place to the *electric effluvium*, which proceeded from the excited,
or charged, body into the surrounding space. Still later, and a fluid, or two
fluids, acting directly upon itself, or upon matter, or on one another, through
intervening space without the aid of intermediate mechanism, took the place
of the electric effluvium—a step which in itself was, perhaps, hardly an
advance. Then came the time for accurate measurement. The simple
observation of phenomena and of the results of experiment must be the first
step in science, and its importance cannot be over-estimated; but before any
quantity can be said to be known, we must have learned how to *measure* it
and to reproduce it in definite amounts. The great law of electrical action, the
same as that of gravitation—the law of the inverse square—soon followed, as
well as the associated fact that the electrification of a conductor resides
wholly on its surface, and there only in a layer whose thickness is too small to
be discovered. The fundamental laws of electricity having thus been
established, there was no limit to the application of mathematical methods to
the problems of the science, and, in the hands of the French mathematicians,
the theory made rapid advances. George Green, of Sneinton, Nottingham,
introduced the term "potential" in an essay published by subscription, in
Nottingham, in 1828, and to him we are indebted for some of our most
powerful analytical methods of dealing with the subject; but his work
remained unappreciated and almost unknown until many of his theorems had
been rediscovered. But the idea of a body acting where it is not, and without
any conceivable mechanism to connect it with that upon which it operates, is
repulsive to the minds of most; and, however well such a theory may lend
itself to mathematical treatment and its consequences be borne out by
experiment, we still feel that we have not solved the problem until we have
traced out the hidden mechanism. The pull of the bell-rope is followed by the
tinkling of the distant bell, but the young philosopher is not satisfied with
such knowledge, but must learn "what is the particular go of that." This
universal desire found its exponent in Faraday, whose imagination beheld
"lines" or "tubes of force" connecting every body with every other body on
which it acted. To his mind these lines or tubes had just as real an existence as
the bell-wire, and were far better adapted to their special purposes. Maxwell,
as we have seen, not only showed that Faraday's system admitted of the same

rigorous mathematical treatment as the older theory, and stood the test as well, but he gave reality to Faraday's views by picturing a mechanism capable of doing all that Faraday required of it, and of transmitting light as well. Thus the problem of electric, magnetic, and electro-magnetic actions was reduced to that of strains and stresses in a medium the constitution of which was pictured to the imagination. Were this theory verified, we might say that we know at least as much about these actions as we know about the transmission of pressure or tension through a solid.

With regard to the *nature* of electricity, it must be admitted that our knowledge is chiefly negative; but, before deploring this, it is worth while to inquire what we mean by saying that we know what a thing is. A definition describes a thing in terms of other things simpler, or more familiar to us, than itself. If, for instance, we say that heat is a form of energy, we know at once its relationship to matter and to motion, and are content; we have described the constitution of heat in terms of simpler things, which are more familiar to us, and of which we *think* we know the nature. But if we ask what *matter* is, we are unable to define it in terms of anything simpler than itself, and can only trust to daily experience to teach us more and more of its properties; unless, indeed, we accept the theory of the vortex atoms of Thomson and Helmholtz. This theory, which has recently been considerably extended by Professor J. J. Thomson, the present occupier of Clerk Maxwell's chair in the University of Cambridge, supposes the existence of a perfect fluid, filling all space, in which minute whirlpools, or vortices, which in a perfect fluid can be created or destroyed only by superhuman agency, form material atoms. These are *atoms*, that is to say, they defy any attempts to sever them, not because they are infinitely hard, but because they have an infinite capacity for *wriggling*, and thus avoid direct contact with any other atoms that come in their way. Perhaps a theory of electricity consistent with this theory of matter may be developed in the future; but, setting aside these theories, we may possibly say that we know as much about electricity as we know about matter; for while we are conversant with many of the properties of each, we *know* nothing of the ultimate nature of either.

But while the theory of electricity has scarcely advanced beyond the point at which it was left by Clerk Maxwell, the practical applications of the science have experienced great developments of late years. Less than a century ago the lightning-rod was the only practical outcome of electrical investigations which could be said to have any real value. Œrsted's discovery, in 1820, of the action of a current on a magnet, led, in the hands of Wheatstone, Cooke, and others, to the development of the electric telegraph. Sir William Thomson's employment of a beam of light reflected from a tiny mirror attached to the magnet of the galvanometer enabled signals to be read when only extremely feeble currents were available, and thus rendered submarine telegraphy possible through very great distances. The discovery by Arago and Davy, that a current of electricity flowing in a coil surrounding an iron bar would convert the bar into a magnet, at once rendered possible a variety of contrivances whereby a current of electricity could be employed to produce small reciprocating movements, or even continuous rotation, where not much power was required, at a distance from the battery. An illustration of the former is found in the common electric bell; it is only necessary that the vibrating armature should form part of the circuit of the electro-magnet, and be so arranged that, while it is held away from the magnet by a spring, it completes the battery circuit, but breaks the connection as soon as it moves towards the magnet under the magnetic attraction. To produce continuous rotation, a number of iron bars may be attached to a fly-wheel, and pass very close to the poles of the magnet without touching them; when a bar is near the magnet, and approaching it, contact should be made in the circuit, but should be broken, so that the magnet may lose its power, as soon as the bar has passed the poles; or the continuous rotation may be produced from an oscillating armature by any of the mechanical contrivances usually adopted for the conversion of reciprocating into continuous circular motion. But all such motors are extremely wasteful in their employment of energy. Faraday's discovery of the rotation of a wire around a magnetic pole laid the foundation for a great variety of electro-motors, in some of which the efficiency has attained a very high standard. About ten years ago, Clerk Maxwell said that the greatest discovery of recent times was the "reversibility" of the Gramme machine, that is, the possibility of causing the armature to rotate between the field-magnets by sending a current through the coils. The electro-motors of to-day differ but little from dynamos in the principles of their construction. The copper disc spinning between the poles of a magnet while an electric current was sent from the centre to the circumference, or *vice versâ*, formed the simplest electro-motor. All the later motors are simply modifications of this, designed to increase the efficiency or power of the machine. Similarly, the earliest machine for the production of an electric current at the expense of mechanical power only, but through the intervention of a permanent magnet, was the rotating disc of Faraday, described on page 262. This contrivance, however, caused a waste of nearly all the energy employed, for while there was an electro-motive force from the centre to the circumference, or in the reverse direction, in that part of the disc which was passing between the poles of the magnet, the current so generated found its readiest return path through the other portions of the disc, and very little traversed the galvanometer or other external circuit. This source of waste could be, for the most part, got rid of by cutting the disc into a number of separate rays, or spokes, and filling up the spaces between them with insulating material. The current then generated in the disc would be obliged to complete its circuit through the external conductor. If we can so arrange matters as to employ at once several turns of a continuous wire in place of one arm, or ray, of the copper disc, we may multiply in a corresponding manner the electro-motive force induced by a given speed of rotation. All magneto-electric generators are simply contrivances with this object. The iron cores frequently employed within the coils of the armature tend to concentrate the lines of force of the magnet, causing a greater number to pass through the coils in certain positions than would pass through them were no iron present. The electro-motive force of such a generator depends on the strength of the magnetic field, the length of wire employed in cutting the lines of force, and the speed with which the wire moves across these lines. The point to aim at in constructing an armature is to make the resistance as small as possible consistent with the electro-motive force required. As there is a limit to the strength of the magnetic field, it follows that for strong currents, where thick wire must be employed, the generator must be made of large dimensions, or the armature must be driven at very high speed to enable a shorter length of wire to be used.

The so-called "compound-interest principle," by which a very small charge of electricity might be employed to develop a very large one by the help of mechanical power, was first applied about a century ago in the revolving doubler. Long afterwards, Sir William Thomson availed himself of the same principle in the construction of the "mouse-mill," or replenisher. The Holtz machine, the Voss and Wimshurst machines, and the other induction-machines of the same class, all work on this principle. It may be illustrated as follows: Take two canisters, call them A and B, and place them on glass supports. Let a very small positive charge be given to A, B remaining uncharged. Now take a brass ball, supported by a silk string. Place it inside A, and let it touch its interior surface. The ball will, as shown by Franklin, Cavendish, and Faraday, remain uncharged. Now raise it near the top of the canister, and, while there, touch it. The ball will become negatively electrified, because the small positive charge in A will attract negative electricity from the earth into the ball. Take the ball, with its negative charge, still hanging by the silk thread, and lower it into B till it touches the bottom. It will give all its charge to B, which will thus acquire a slight negative charge. Raise the ball till it is near the top of B, and then touch it with the finger or a metal rod. It will receive a positive charge from the earth because of the attraction of the negative charge on B. Now remove the ball and let it again touch the interior of A. It will give up all its charge to A; and then, repeating the whole cycle of operations, the charge carried on the ball will be greater than before, and increase in each successive operation, the electrification increasing in geometrical progression like compound interest. A Leyden jar having one coating connected to A and the other to B, may thus be highly charged in course of time. A pair of carrier balls or plates, or a number of pairs, may be used instead of one. The carriers, just before leaving A and B, may be put in contact with one another instead of being put to earth; they may be mounted on a revolving shaft, and the forms of A and B modified to admit of the revolution of the carriers, and all the necessary contacts may be made automatically. We thus get various forms of the continuous electrophorus, and if the carriers are mounted on glass plates, and rows of points placed alongside the springs or brushes used for making the contacts, when the charges on the carriers become very strong, electricity will be radiated from the points on to the revolving glass plates, which will thus themselves take the place of the metal carriers. Such is the action in the Voss and other similar machines.

But after Faraday had shown how to construct a magneto-electric machine, the idea of applying the "compound-interest principle," and thus converting the magneto-electric machine into the "dynamo," occurred apparently simultaneously and independently to Siemens, Varley, and Wheatstone. The first dynamo constructed by Wheatstone is still in the museum of King's College, London. Wilde employed a magneto-electric machine to generate a current which was used to excite the electro-magnet of a similar but larger machine, having an electro-magnet instead of a permanent steel magnet. The electro-magnet could be made much larger and stronger than the steel magnet, and from its armature, when made to revolve by steam power, a correspondingly stronger current could be maintained. The idea which occurred to Siemens, Varley, and Wheatstone was to use the whole, or a part, of the current produced by the armature to excite its own electro-magnet, and thus to dispense with the magneto-electric machine which served as the separate exciter. When a part only of the current is thus employed, and is set apart entirely for this duty, the machine is a "shunt dynamo;" when the whole of the current traverses the field-magnet coils as well as the external circuit, it is a "series dynamo." The apparent difficulty lies in starting the current, but a mass of iron once magnetized always retains a certain amount of "residual magnetism," unless special means are taken to get rid of it, and even then the earth's magnetism would generally induce sufficient in the iron to start the action. Commencing, then, with a slight trace of residual magnetism, the revolution of the armature generates a feeble current, which passing round the magnet coils, strengthens the magnetism, whereupon a stronger current is generated, which in turn makes the magnet still stronger, and so on until the magnet becomes saturated or the limit of power of the engine is reached, and the speed begins to diminish, or a condition of affairs is reached at which an increased current in the armature injures the magnetic field as much as the corresponding increase in the field-magnet coils strengthens it, and then no further increase of current will take place without increasing the speed of rotation. In a true dynamo the whole of the energy, both of the current and of the electro-magnets, is obtained from the source of power employed in driving the machine.

But Faraday's discovery of electro-magnetic induction led to practical developments in other directions. Graham Bell placed a thin iron disc in front of the pole of a bar magnet, and wound a coil of fine wire round the bar very near the pole. The ends of the coils of two such instruments he connected together. When the iron disc of one instrument approached the pole of the magnet, the lines of force were disturbed, fewer escaped radially from the bar, and more left it at the end, so as to go straight to the iron disc; thus the number of lines of force passing through the coil was altered, and a current was induced which, passing round the coil of the other instrument, strengthened or weakened its magnet, and caused the iron disc to approach it or recede from it, according to the way in which the coils were coupled. Thus the movements of the first disc were faithfully repeated by the second, and the minute vibrations set up in the disc by sound-waves were all faithfully repeated by the second instrument. This was Graham Bell's telephone, in which the transmitter and receiver were convertible.

But another and an earlier application of Faraday's discoveries is found in the induction coil. A short length of thick wire and a very great length of thin wire are wound upon an iron bar. The ends of the long thin wire, or secondary coil, form the terminals of the machine; the short thick wire, or primary coil, is connected with a battery, but in the circuit is placed an "interrupter." This is generally a small piece of iron, or hammer, mounted on a steel spring opposite one end of the iron core, the spring pressing the hammer back against a screw the end of which, like the back of the hammer, is tipped with platinum; and this contact completes the battery circuit. When the current starts, the iron core becomes a magnet, attracts the hammer, breaks the contact, stops the current, the magnetism dies away, the hammer is forced back by the spring, and then the cycle of events is repeated. But the starting of the current in the primary causes a great many lines of magnetic force to pass through each of the many thousand turns of wire in the secondary, especially as the iron core conducts most of the lines of force of each turn of the primary almost from end to end of the coil, and thus through nearly all the turns of the secondary. This action might be further increased by connecting the ends of the iron core with an iron tube or series of longitudinal bars placed outside the whole coil. When the primary current ceases, all these lines of force vanish. Thus during the starting of the primary current, which, on account of self-induction, occupies a considerable time, there will be an inverse current in the secondary proportional to the rate of increase of the primary; and while the primary is dying away, there will be a direct current in the secondary proportional to its rate of decrease. The primary current cannot be increased at a faster rate than corresponds to the power of the battery, but by making a very sharp break it may be stopped very rapidly. Still, however rapidly the circuit is broken, self-induction causes a spark to fly across the gap until the energy of the current is used up. The introduction of the condenser, consisting of a number of sheets of tinfoil insulated by paper steeped in paraffin wax, and connected alternately with one end or the other of the primary coil, serves to increase the rapidity with which the primary current died away, by rapidly using up its energy in charging the condenser, and produces a corresponding diminution in the spark at the contact-breaker. This rapid destruction of the primary current causes a correspondingly great electro-motive force in the secondary coil, and thus very long sparks are produced between the terminals of the secondary coil when the primary current is broken, though no such sparks are produced when the primary current starts. If the secondary coil be connected up with a galvanometer, so that there is a metallic circuit throughout, it will be found that just as much electricity flows in one direction through the circuit at the break of the primary as flows in the other direction at the make, the difference being that the first is a very strong current of great electro-motive force but lasting a very short time, the second a feebler current lasting a correspondingly longer time.

But though the recent advances in electrical science have been very great, the grandest triumph of this century is the establishment of the principle of the conservation of energy, which has settled for ever the problem of "the perpetual motion," by showing that it has no solution. This problem was not simply to find a mechanism which should for ever move, but one from which energy might be continuously derived for the performance of external work— in fact, an engine which should require no fuel. But in spite of all that has been proved, numbers of patents are annually taken out for contrivances to effect this object.

We have seen how Rumford showed that heat was motion, and how he approximately determined its mechanical equivalent. Séguin, a nephew of Montgolfier, endeavoured to show that, when a steam-engine was working, less heat entered the condenser than when the same amount of steam was blown idly through the engine. This Hirn succeeded in showing, thus proving that heat was actually used up in doing work. Mayer, of Heilbronn, measured the work done in compressing air, and the heat generated by the compression, and assumed that the whole of the work done in the compression, and no more, was converted into the heat developed, which was the same thing as assuming that no work was done in altering the positions of the particles of gas. From these measurements he deduced a value of the mechanical equivalent of heat. The assumption which Mayer made was shown experimentally by Joule to be nearly correct. Joule proved that, when air expands from a high pressure into a vacuum, no heat is generated or absorbed on the whole. This he did by compressing air in an iron bottle, which was connected with another bottle from which the air had been exhausted, the connecting tube being closed by a stop-cock. The whole apparatus was immersed in a bath of water, and on allowing the air to rush from one vessel into the other, and then stirring the water, the temperature was found to be the same as before. When the iron bottles were in separate baths of water, that from which the air rushed was cooled, and that into which it rushed was heated to the same extent. Joule and Thomson afterwards showed that a very small amount of heat is absorbed in this experiment. Joule also showed that the heat generated in a battery circuit is proportional to the product of the electro-motive force and the current, or to the product of the resistance and the square of the current, which, in virtue of Ohm's law, is the same thing. This relation is often known as Joule's law. He also proved that, for the same amount of chemical action in the battery, the heat generated was the same, whether it were all generated within the battery or part in the battery and part in an external wire; and that in the latter case, if the wire became so hot as to emit light, the heat measured was less than before, on account of the energy radiated as light. With a magneto-electric machine he employed mechanical power to produce a current, and the energy of the current he converted into heat. In all cases he found that, *whatever transformations the energy might undergo in its course, a definite amount of mechanical energy, if entirely converted into heat, always produced the same amount of heat*; and he thereby proved, not only that heat is essentially *motion*, but that it corresponds precisely with that particular dynamical quantity which is called *energy*; and thus justified the attempt to find a relation between heat and energy, or to express the mechanical equivalent of heat as so many foot-pounds.

Joule then set to work to determine, in the most accurate manner possible, the number of foot-pounds of work which, if entirely converted into heat, would raise one pound of water through 1° Fahr. The best known of his experiments is that in which he caused a paddle to revolve by means of a falling weight, and thereby to churn a quantity of water contained in a cylindrical vessel, the rotation of the water being prevented by fixed vanes. In these experiments he allowed for the work done outside the vessel of water or calorimeter, for the buoyancy of the air on the descending weight, and for the energy still retained by the weight when it struck the floor. From the results obtained he deduced 772 foot-pounds as the mechanical equivalent of heat. Expressed in terms of the Centigrade scale, Joule's equivalent, that is, the number of foot-pounds of work in the latitude of Manchester, which, if entirely converted into heat, will raise one pound of water 1° C., is 1390.

Joule's experiments show that the same amount of energy always corresponds to, and can be converted into, the same amount of heat, and that no transformations, electrical or other, can ever increase or diminish this quantity. Maxwell expressed this principle as follows:—

The energy of a system is a quantity which can neither be increased nor diminished by any actions taking place between the parts of the system, though it may be transformed into any of the forms of which energy is susceptible.

This is the great principle of the conservation of energy which is applicable equally to all branches of science.

Another principle, almost equally general in its applicability, is that of the dissipation of energy, for which we are indebted in the first instance to Sir William Thomson. All forms of energy may be converted into heat, and heat tends so to diffuse itself throughout all bodies as to bring them to one uniform temperature. This is its ultimate state of degradation, and from that state no methods with which we are acquainted can transform any portion of it. When energy is possessed by a system in consequence of the relative positions or motions of bodies which we can handle, and whose movements we may control, the whole of the energy may be employed in doing any work we please; in fact, it is all *available* for our purpose, or its *availability* may be said to be perfect. Energy in any other form is limited in its availability by the conditions under which we can place it. For example, the energy of chemical action in a battery may be used to produce a current, and this to drive a motor by which mechanical work is effected, but some of the energy must inevitably be degraded into the form of heat by the resistance of the battery and of the conductor, and this portion will be greater as the rate of doing work is increased. The ratio of the quantity of energy which can be employed for mechanical purposes with the means at our disposal, to the whole amount present, is called the *availability* of the energy. All forms of energy may be wholly converted into heat, but only a fraction of any quantity of heat can be transformed into higher forms of energy, and this depends on the temperature of the source of heat and of the coldest body which can be employed as a condenser, being greater the greater the difference between the temperatures of the source and condenser, and the lower the temperature of the latter. In every operation which takes place in nature there is a degradation of energy, and though some portion of the energy may be raised in availability, another portion is lowered, so that on the whole the availability is diminished. Thus, in the case of the heat-engine, work can be obtained from heat only by allowing another portion of the heat to fall in temperature; and, as originally stated by Sir William Thomson, "it is impossible, by means of inanimate material agency, to obtain mechanical effect from any portion of matter by cooling it below the temperature of the coldest of the surrounding objects," and to leave the working substance in the same condition in which it was at the commencement of the operations. Accepting this principle, Professor James Thomson showed that increase of pressure must lower the freezing point of water, for otherwise it would be possible to construct an engine which, working by the expansion of water in freezing, would continue to do work by cooling a body below the temperature of any other body available, and he calculated the amount of pressure necessary to lower the freezing point through one degree. The conclusion was afterwards experimentally verified by Sir William Thomson, and served to explain all the phenomena of regelation. Thus, like the principle of the conservation of energy, the principle of the dissipation of energy serves as a guide in the search after truth. But there is this difference between the two principles—no one can conceive of any method by which to circumvent the conservation of energy; but Clerk Maxwell showed that the principle of dissipation of energy might be overridden by the exercise of intelligence on the part of any creature whose faculties were sufficiently delicate to deal with individual molecules. In the case of gases, the temperature depends on the average energy of motion of the individual particles, and heat consists simply of this motion; but in any mass of gas, whatever the average energy may be, some of the particles will be moving with very great, and some with very small, velocities. By imagining two portions of gas, originally at the same temperature, separated by a partition containing trap-doors which could be opened or closed without expenditure of energy, and supposing a "demon" placed in charge of each door, who would open the door whenever a particle was approaching very rapidly from one side, or very slowly from the other, but keep it shut under other circumstances, he showed that it would be possible to sort the particles, so that those in the one compartment should have a great velocity, and those in the other a small one. Hence, out of a mass of gas at uniform temperature, two portions might be obtained, one at a high temperature and the other at a low, and, by means of a heat-engine, work could be obtained until the two portions were again at equal temperatures, when the services of the "demons" might be again taken advantage of, and the operations repeated until all the heat was used up.

Any theory which is brought forward to explain a phenomenon, or any process which is proposed to effect any operation, must in the first instance submit to the test of the application of these two principles of conservation and dissipation of energy; and any proposal which fails to bear these tests may be at once rejected. The essential feature of the science of to-day is its quantitative character. We must, for instance, not only know that radiant energy comes to us from the sun, but we must learn how much energy is annually received by the earth in this way; and, in the next place, how much energy is radiated by the sun in all directions in the same time. When we have learned this, we want to know what is the source of this energy; and no theory of the sun which does not enable us to explain how this constant expenditure of energy is maintained can be accepted. Last century it was possible to believe, with Sir William Herschel, that the greater part of the sun's mass is comparatively cool, and that it is surrounded by only a thin sheet of flame. To-day such a theory would be rejected at once, simply because the thin shell of flame could not provide energy for the solar radiation for any considerable time. The contact theory of the galvanic cell, as originally enunciated, fell to the ground for a similar reason. The simple contact of dissimilar metals could afford no continuous supply of energy to sustain the current. Applied to the steam-engine, the doctrine of energy teaches us, not only that, corresponding to the combustion of a pound of coal, there is a definite quantity of work which is the mechanical equivalent of the heat generated, and is such that no engine of which we can conceive is capable of deriving from the combustion of the pound of coal a greater amount of work, but it teaches us that there is a further limitation fixed to the amount of work obtainable. This limitation depends upon the range of temperature at our command; and, when the range is known, we can express the amount of energy realizable by a perfect engine working through that range as a definite fraction of the whole energy corresponding to the heat of combustion of the fuel. Thus, if we find that a particular engine realizes only 15 per cent. of the energy of its fuel in work done, we must not suppose that mechanical improvements in the engine would enable us to realize any considerable portion of the other 85 per cent.; for it may be that a theoretically perfect engine, working with its boiler and condenser at the same temperatures as those of the engine considered, could only realize 25 per cent. of the energy of the fuel, reducing the margin for improvement from 85 to 10 per cent., as long as the range of temperature is unaltered. To improve the efficiency beyond this limit, the range of temperature must be increased, that is, generally, hotter steam must be used.

The principles of energy are thus guides, not only to the scientific theorist, but to the practical engineer, and they have been established only through careful measurement. The simple observation of phenomena, and of the conditions under which they occur, could never have led to the establishment of such principles; and, though the carrying out of experiments which do not involve measurements is of great value, it is the careful measurement, however simple, which affords the highest training to the mind and hand, and without which any course of instruction in experimental physics is of little value.

The Hindoos used to regard the earth as a vast dome carried on the backs of elephants. The elephants themselves, however, required support, and were represented as standing on the back of a gigantic tortoise. It does not, however, appear that any support was provided for the tortoise. In some respects this figure represents the apparently perpetual condition of scientific knowledge. Phenomena are investigated, and are shown to depend upon other actions which appear simpler or more fundamental than the phenomena at first observed. These, again, are found to obey laws which are of much wider application, or appear to be still more fundamental; but it may be that we are as far off as ever from discovering the great secret of the universe, the ultimate nature of all things.